THE ANIMALS CAME TO DRINK

The giant crocodile

Frontispiece]

The Animals Came to Drink

BY

CHERRY KEARTON

Author of
"The Island of Penguins"
"In the Land of the Lion"
"My Friend Toto"
Etc., Etc.

WITH 42 PHOTOGRAPHS BY THE AUTHOR

LONGMANS, GREEN AND CO.
LONDON ♦ NEW YORK ♦ TORONTO
1932

LONGMANS, GREEN AND CO. LTD.
39 PATERNOSTER ROW, LONDON, E.C.4
6 OLD COURT HOUSE STREET, CALCUTTA
53 NICOL ROAD, BOMBAY
36A MOUNT ROAD, MADRAS

LONGMANS, GREEN AND CO.
55 FIFTH AVENUE, NEW YORK
221 EAST 20TH STREET, CHICAGO
88 TREMONT STREET, BOSTON
128-132 UNIVERSITY AVENUE, TORONTO

Made in Great Britain

AUTHOR'S NOTE

TO some of my readers who are not ac-
quainted with Africa and its animal life,
certain of the more sensational episodes in this
story may appear incredible. It is to them that
this Note is addressed.

Nowadays it is customary for writers of stories
to preface their work with a statement that all the
characters are fictitious and all the incidents
imaginary. That is not the case here. I have the
best of reasons for knowing, for instance, that
the giant crocodile is not fictitious, for I took
his photograph nineteen years ago whilst crossing
Africa from East to West; indeed, I have photo-
graphed every character in the book. As to the
incidents, each of them is in strict accord with
natural history as I have myself studied it by day
and by night during thirty-two years among wild
life in Africa.

My purpose in writing is, through the medium
of a story, to describe the natural life of animals

9

in Africa—particularly before that life is changed through the presence of the white man.

I should be thankful if this book could act as a counterblast to the many animal stories, so constantly appearing, which are based on utterly false or distorted natural history. It seems that such falsity in no way detracts from their success; and the same thing is true in the world of the cinematograph, where double exposure and many other devices are used to show animals in unnatural situations and to give the effect of their behaving as, in fact, they never behave. The people who try to give us "sensations" both in films and in books appear to imagine that "art" is needed in that respect to supply the defects of Nature; that the wild life of animals is sadly in need of a little "gingering up."

Perhaps this book may serve its purpose in showing that truth, among the animals of Africa, is not merely stranger than fiction, but is at least its equal in interest and excitement.

CHERRY KEARTON.

CONTENTS

CHAPTER		PAGE
I.	A Valley in Africa	17
II.	Shadows in the River	21
III.	Crocodile and Man	26
IV.	Crocodile's Journey	35
V.	Crocodile and Leopard	41
VI.	The Leopard Hunts	47
VII.	The Graceful Impalla	54
VIII.	Among the Baboons	60
IX.	The Fire	69
X.	The Lion Cubs	78
XI.	Lions Hunt by Night	87
XII.	Crocodiles in the Creek	94
XIII.	Impalla and Zebra	102
XIV.	The Hyena Goes Home	113
XV.	The Mother Giraffe	120
XVI.	The Wild Dogs	130
XVII.	Elephants	136
XVIII.	Crocodile Eggs	147

CONTENTS

CHAPTER   PAGE

XIX. THE RIVAL BABOONS . . . 152

XX. CROCODILE AND RHINOCEROS: A
        DUEL OF GIANTS . . . 160

XXI. IMPALLA'S JOY 168

XXII. CROCODILES AT WAR . . . 173

XXIII. RAIN 187

LIST OF ILLUSTRATIONS

THE GIANT CROCODILE . . . . *Frontispiece*

"He was a giant, ugly and ungainly . . ." . . ⎱ FACING PAGE

". . . but the embodiment of strength and invulnerability . . . . . . ⎰ 32

"An ostrich that was no ostrich" . . . 33

"Monkeys stood up to stare . . ." . . . ⎱ 36
". . . as the crocodile passed" . . . . ⎰

"Silent and with startled eyes". . . . 37

THE SANDBANK—"here there would be food in plenty" 44

"The river broadened into a deep oval pool" . 45

"She stayed on the sandbank to drink" . . ⎱ 53
"An ugly shape, evil and horrible" . . . ⎰

"The impalla was extremely graceful" . . 54

"His eyes fastened on her as he began to creep closer" . . . . ⎱ 70
BABOONS—"The males chattered as if in argument" ⎰

"The old leader would climb a tree". . . 71

13

LIST OF ILLUSTRATIONS

FACING PAGE

"A cheetah leapt down from the rocks" . . 74

"The fire was sweeping forward" . . ⎫
                                       ⎬ 75
"The thunder of the hoofs of stampeding animals" ⎭

THE LION 86

"The lion restlessly got to his feet" . . . 87

"The lion stood looking back across the way they
　　had come" 90

"His excited purr brought the lioness to her feet" 91

"A fine-looking creature" 112

"The young impalla kept close beside the zebra". ⎫
                                                   ⎬ 113
"The impalla stayed with the zebra" . . . ⎭

"With their tails twirling aloft in the air they
　　raced away" 128

"The mother giraffe" 129

"Lapping eagerly, but always watchful" . . ⎫
                                             ⎬ 130
"The blurred grey outline of a herd of elephants" ⎭

"The impalla moved to one side of the herd" . 131

"Something moved, like the end of a log" . . 142

"The baby crocodiles were less than four inches
　　long" 143

THE BABOON 164

"The rhinoceros lowered his head to browse" . 165

"There, walking across the alternate bars of sun
　　and shade, went a herd of impalla" . . 172

LIST OF ILLUSTRATIONS

FACING PAGE

" The gazelles grazed onward in the direction of the
river " . . . .
" The impalla, her own herd of impalla, the friends
she had lost and now regained " . . . } 173

" For several minutes his tail continued to churn
the water " 184

" A feathered hedge appeared about the carcase " . 185

CHAPTER
ONE

A VALLEY IN AFRICA

MAN, who takes possession one by one of the wild parts of the earth and replaces jungle with pasture land, primeval forests with houses and streets, had not yet set his mark on that valley; neither roads nor bridges nor homes were to be seen anywhere between the broken range of hills that bounded it to the south and the mountains on the north. Three miles westward, on the open plain beyond the last hill, lay a native village; another stood on the foothills of the mountains. But each had water and food close at hand, and although an occasional party of men might come down to the river that marked the centre of the valley, the undulating slopes on either side of the water remained the undisturbed domain of wild creatures.

Between the two ranges of hills, the ground sloped at first gradually and then more steeply to the banks of the river. The earth was covered for the most part with brownish-green grass, sometimes growing to the height of a man's hips. Here and there grew solitary thorn trees; in patches the country was closely wooded; rocky, isolated hills of volcanic origin stood up sharply out of the ground; and the centre of the valley showed a long, narrow, winding patch of tangled undergrowth and trees, through which the river ran, now smoothly between high banks and now murmuring over rapids.

On the higher of the rocky hills lived the rhinoceros and the leopard; on smaller crags the baboons slept or chattered or played games; on the plain lived lion, giraffe, buffalo, zebra and many sorts of buck; in the river were hippo, crocodiles and turtles; everywhere were birds and many coloured insects.

The valley was still as Nature had made it, verdant, entangled, the home of creatures who had not yet learnt the unnatural wariness which comes inevitably where man has hunted. Yet it was not peaceful. Fear and suspicion ruled it by day and by night. The old rhinoceros who lived on the crest of a ridge not far from the river, might stand drowsing under a thorn tree

18

through the heat of the day, secure from danger while he felt the parasite birds on his back; but if they rose he would be on guard, sniffing uncertainly and in doubt as to the danger and the direction from which it threatened. On the plain at the foot of the ridge, kongoni, zebra and impalla would feed, but one of each herd would stand aside—a sentinel. Further from the river, where the thorn trees dotted the ground, the giraffe would nibble at leaves or, spread-eagling their legs, would bend their long necks to drink at pools; but always they would be watchful lest the neighbouring grass should stir with the movements of an enemy.

For the lion would hunt there, and the leopard would lie on a crag seeking his prey. The hyena and the jackal would wait for the remnants of the kill, and the vultures would soar in the heights of the air, eternally waiting for the moment when they would swoop down to finish the scavenging. The cheetah roamed through plain and forest, the python waited along the branches of trees, the monitor unearthed and devoured the eggs of the crocodile, the hyena and the lion carried off the young of ostriches. No creature could eat or drink without fear. Animals coming to drink at the river or at pools would hesitate, stand motionless, even go back as they had come, with thirst unquenched. The grunt of the hunting lion or the cough of the leopard would sound at night across the valley, bringing terror to the gazelles or the baboons; or the silent crocodile would stir the river as it came to snatch its prey.

CHAPTER
TWO

SHADOWS IN THE RIVER

FROM the village of mud and stick huts which stood on the lower slope of the mountain, came a party of natives, the sun, directly overhead, gleaming on the blades of their spears, on the short-handled axes which some of them carried, and on the polished surface of their shoulders.

They marched in single file, pressing down the grass into a narrow, uneven lane in which the less trampled blades would eventually raise themselves until only a faintly ruffled line marked the fact that men had trodden there. Everywhere else, the grass showed an unbroken surface of dying green, moving gently to the breeze.

The men came forward warily, keeping watch for any sudden movement of the grass which would betray the presence of danger; for the grass was here more than three feet high—ample cover for a hunting animal. Once the leader halted, pointing to the left where the blades of grass seemed to sway more violently than did those around them; but nothing showed above the surface and presently the small creature whose movement had stirred the grass moved away, his route marked by a shaking, zigzag line which at last faded into the distance.

Advancing once more, the men came at last through a belt of trees and undergrowth to a spot where the river met a series of small islands and broke into four smaller channels which, after winding through higher ground, eventually reunited. There a bridge could be built, each of the four streams being spanned by a hewn tree. Standing on the bank, they chose a tree whose branches would reach to the first of the series of islands. Then with their axes they set to work.

The river at this spot, within the belt of trees, ran between steep banks, eight feet high and overhung with vegetation; the pale-backed leaves of the wild banana were crossed by long slender branches of palms drooping towards the water, while a tangled undergrowth grew between the trunks of trees and hid the edge of the river bank. The bigger trees spread their branches over the water, meeting those from the opposite bank, so that overhead was a lace-work of brown and green, while below, the surface of the water was deeply shadowed. The river ran through the darkness of a deep channel, so black and silent that it might have suggested the unseen presence of something forbidding and of evil purpose.

.   .   .   .   .

The surface of the water stirred slightly. With no sound that the men working above could detect, a small, uneven square of darkness moved, detaching itself from the surrounding blackness, crossing here a patch of grey and there a narrow streak of sunlight, then disappearing altogether into further shadows, and finally seeming to rest in a big swirling pool a hundred yards lower down the stream. There was a stir as if some huge body turned slowly beneath the water, and then the head and body of a crocodile rose above the surface. For a few seconds they remained just out of the water, then slowly sank until only the blunt-shaped snout and the small, Asiatically sloping eyes remained.

The crocodile lay perfectly still on a narrow ledge that projected under water from the bank. The webbed claws at the end of his stumpy feet

dug into the sand that had settled thinly on the
rock, his body sagged to rest on the ledge, his
enormous tail stretched out into the depths.
From jaw to tail he measured twenty-four feet—
more than twice the length of either of the other
crocodiles that lived in that part of the river.
He was a giant, even of his race, ugly and ungainly, but the embodiment of strength and invulnerability.

Because of his huge size, he could not be
content with a diet of fish, only occasionally
supplemented with flesh, which satisfied the
smaller crocodiles. He needed meat as his main
food, eking it out with a fish here and there
snapped at half thoughtlessly as he floated in
the water. Consequently he went more frequently
to the sandbank, taking animals as they came to
drink. His presence was a never-ceasing danger
to the antelope, the gazelle, and other creatures
that came to the edge of the river.

Now, a few minutes earlier he had been
slumbering at the surface of the water, fresh from
a hearty meal. Probably it was a sound from the
bank above that had awakened him. He had
looked up, to see something moving on the bank
—black against the darkness of tree trunks and

undergrowth, a moving silhouette—and then, surprisingly, since there was only a gentle breeze, a
tree had crashed, falling across the stream so that
its upper branches touched the further bank and
others stirred the water in which the crocodile
lay. He did not know what caused the tree to
fall; nor did he definitely connect its falling with
the figures that moved upon the bank. But
instinct told him of danger and he moved to
greater safety, down the stream.

Now, as he lay in darkness and security, he was
interested, not so much in the fallen tree as in
the thought of those figures which he realised
were neither buck nor baboon, but something
new in his experience. One day he would try
the flavour of them. They might prove quite
different from gazelle or zebra, possibly more tasty
than the carcase of a hippopotamus. At some
time or other they would doubtless come down
to the river to drink like the other creatures of
the bank, and then he would be waiting, just in
the shadows. . . .

CHAPTER
THREE

CROCODILE AND MAN

WITH the making of the bridge, life changed on that section of the river.

Men and women now crossed almost daily, sometimes hurrying across as if anxious to reach the end of a journey made for purposes of trade and to set down burdens which four miles in the heat of the sun had made unduly heavy; sometimes stopping to rest within sight of the water.

Now and then one would come to a small sandbank a hundred yards downstream and stoop to fill a gourd—and then two others would stand on guard, with spears upraised, watching for the approach of crocodiles. And the crocodiles were there—the giant and two others—lying in the deepest of shadows, with their small eyes fixed on those figures which moved so temptingly. A woman would come across the sandbank, barely to the edge of the water, stoop,

26

and then return, the water spilling over the edge of her gourd as she carried it aslant in her haste. But once, as evening was falling, one came with an earthen pot, and after she had filled it she lingered, her hands in the stream, splashing the cool water against her legs. The giant crocodile, moving swiftly from the shadows and submerged except for eyes and nostrils, made but a ripple on the surface as he drew near. In another second his jaws would have opened and closed—but there was a man's hoarse shout, another, the woman turned with a shriek and the pot fell into the water. Then a spear struck the crocodile's head, half stunning him, and as he floated out into the centre of the stream, in his returning consciousness he felt a sudden sharp jab of pain behind the socket of his right front leg.

He swam swiftly, then, hardly noticing at first a sense of dragging on his right side. But when he went more slowly, in the security of lower reaches of the river, he felt the pain with every movement of that limb; and he found that something thin and hard still projected from his hide, its head embedded in his body. And while he rested, wondering, his leg grew stiff and ached.

Days passed. By scraping against a rocky piece

of the river bank, he succeeded at last in breaking the embedded spear, but the metal head remained fast in his hide, a festering wound. In time, the pain lessened, and he recovered nearly the full use of his leg. But there remained occasional stiffness and now and then an ache. He remembered, and became even more wary than before.

The animals on the bank and the plain also found that the coming of men added to the dangers of their life. The men neglected no chance to kill. Often as they marched they would pause at the sight of some small buck and then would spread out silently into a deep half-circle and advance through the grass, cutting off one animal from the others, surrounding it and killing it. Hardly a day passed without the load-carriers having their burdens increased by some carcase for the pot, killed by the armed men who marched in advance of the rest.

A herd of water-buck, which had lost several of its number, one day moved to a clump of trees half a mile further from the bridge. Near by, another sandbank sloped down to the stream, and there the water-buck went in greater safety to drink. In a few days they were joined by a herd of gazelles and then by zebra and kongoni;

the news of safety quickly spread. Presently the land beside the bridge was deserted, save for monkeys, rock-rabbits, birds and monitors—the creatures that were safe in trees or burrowed fortresses.

The giant crocodile, realising amazedly that animals no longer came to drink at the sandbank on which he had taken toll for many years, sought his prey both up the stream and down, and at last discovered the new drinking place. But there the river ran shallower and more swiftly, and there was little overhanging foliage to cast protecting shadows on the water. Thrice in succession, as the crocodile swam towards the sandbank, noiselessly and always with an instinctive caution, a watchful baboon cried out or a shy zebra on the brink turned suddenly to flee; and then in a wild scamper, buck, gazelles and all dashed off towards the open grass and left the river to solitary darkness and a hungry crocodile.

Food then became urgently necessary. Even the two smaller crocodiles missed the occasional gazelle and buck that they were accustomed to capture, and became anxious for meat; while for the giant something near to starvation soon threatened. When, on very rare occasions, the body of a dead hippopotamus floated down the stream, it could presently be dragged below the water, to serve as a feast. But the live, fully grown hippopotamus was untouchable. And when the animals had ceased to come to the river to drink at places easily accessible to waiting crocodiles, there was nothing left except the rare chance of hippo meat and those unsufficing fish. Nothing. . . . unless after all it should prove possible to snap at the dark, smooth legs of the creatures beside the bridge.

.   .   .   .   .

As the heat of the day advanced the giant crocodile gradually raised himself out of the water on the further side of the river from the sandbank, and came to rest a few yards from the edge. There, beside a fallen tree, he lay still, indistinguishable at a distance from the log. But for all his immobility he was alert, watchful, waiting.

Unlike his two companions, who lay in the water, their nostrils on the water-line, their eyes as alert as his own, he chose to attack from the land because experience had taught him that it was there that he was most dangerous. Often in the past, when animals had proved more than usually shy, he had tricked them by silence and stillness until they had approached within half a dozen yards; and then with a sudden turn he had swung his mighty tail, which could knock even a wildebeest from its feet, and in a minute he had been dragging the body of his prey beneath the water.

In the hottest hours the water dried from his hide and his colour changed to a grey that was almost exactly that of the muddy ground on which he rested. Lingering thus out of the water had less and less appeal to him as the heat passed; he was not accustomed to stay on the land except during the hottest part of the day. Yet he did not move. He knew too well that if he was to accomplish his desire he must be wary and immovable.

Suddenly his ears detected a sound that gradually grew louder. The long file of men and women, many of them laden with gourds or earthen pots or bales of tobacco, the profits of the previous day's trading, drew near to the bridge. Two of the warriors, in advance of the rest, came half-way across the stream, then stopped and peered downwards. There was a whispered consultation and a signal. The advancing file stopped. The two men went back as they had come, and for a long time there was silence.

His impatience growing, the giant crocodile on the further bank of the river shifted his tail uneasily. He could no longer make out any of the dark figures by the head of the bridge, but beyond the stream, approaching the sandbank, was now a splash of white. It was an ostrich, not pecking at blades of grass as he would have expected it to do, but with neck and head stiffly upright. An ostrich was poor as food, but better nevertheless than nothing. If the width of the stream had not separated them he would have tried to tempt it into a closer approach.

But no such obstacle deterred the two crocodiles in the river below. They too had seen the ostrich, they too decided that insufficient as it must be it was better than a wasted day. They swam silently to the bank, waited for a second and then dashed out of the water, moving forward at a speed which might have seemed surprising for beasts of such a size.

To the giant that watched across the stream, what followed was puzzling. As the two crocodiles drew so near that in another second their teeth would have closed upon the ostrich's legs,

" An ostrich that was no ostrich."

" He was a giant, ugly and ungainly . . ."

". . . but the embodiment of strength and invulnerability."

the bird seemed suddenly to leap into the air. Then its neck bent sideways, the black feathers on its chest parted and in an amazing transformation a man appeared from within the very body of the bird, throwing back body and feathers to fall with the neck and head in a confused heap beside him.

Spear in hand, the man sprang back, and at the same moment five other men rushed forward from the shelter of the trees. Even as, perhaps, the crocodiles vaguely realised that they had been deceived by an ostrich that was no ostrich, but only a decoy to lure them from the water, spears were cast at them. Immediately the scene was one of turmoil. Two spears missed and passed harmlessly over, but others found their mark. One entered a crocodile's throat, but he broke it instantly; another, well aimed, pierced the eye of the second crocodile, mortally wounding him, but leaving him still able to lash from side to side with his enormous tail, breaking the legs of a man who ventured closer to despatch him, before his muscles grew stiff in death. The other, with the broken haft of a spear still protruding from his jaw, turned towards the water, swinging his tail as he went. But the men followed him, gathering up their fallen spears and driving them into his body at close range. One native, venturing dangerously in his excitement, found his legs knocked from under him by that flail-like tail as it swept with irresistible weight from side to side. But the others, close on the flanks of the crocodile, plunged their spears again and again into the more vulnerable points of his body until, when he had all but reached the comparative safety of the river, the crocodile died at last, a dragon-like monster, outnumbered and defeated, yet terrifying and dangerous even to the last second of his struggles.

CHAPTER
FOUR

CROCODILE'S JOURNEY

LOG-LIKE, the giant crocodile drifted down-stream. With the departure of the animals from the drinking-place at which he had for so long been accustomed to feed, the failure of the attempt to substitute for them the new food of which he had dreamed, and finally the killing of the two other crocodiles, the old stretch of river had become uninhabitable to him. Where all had once been serene, an easy hunting-ground, starvation—or something nearly approaching it —now threatened him. The hollows in which he had been accustomed to store his food were empty and useless; the deep pools, where he had been wont to bask beside the other crocodiles, were now lonely. The time had come when he must seek a new home.

He had no idea where that home would be. His road was the river, and down it, as the current took him, he went, stopping only to explore where there seemed to be chances of good and plentiful food. Here and there, where the water ran shallow, he was forced to walk, with a clumsy gait, his body just clear of the surface and swinging slowly and heavily from side to side. Once, to avoid some rapids, he made his way for a short distance overland. But for the most part he drifted with the current, sometimes dozing as he went, sometimes sufficiently alert to snap at fish whose bodies attracted him as they sped beneath the water.

Beyond the end of the tree-belt the river flowed for a space between low, brownish-green banks which rose on either side to smooth stretches of bare land. Before, he had been screened by two curtains of trees from the view of animals on the banks, and his passage had aroused no interest; no creature had seen him coming and fled in terror. But here, where there was no screen and open stretches of brownish grass sloped gradually to the water's edge, where isolated trees grew upon the banks, and where occasional sandbanks bore the marks of the animals that used them as drinking places, the crocodile was seen and his approach was dreaded.

" Monkeys stood up to stare . . ."

". . . as the crocodile passed."

" Silent and with startled eyes."

Water-buck, impalla, zebra and many smaller creatures raised their heads as they drank and bolted at once to safer distance. Monkeys, chattering and playing under little clumps of trees, stood up to stare at him, then swiftly vanished helter-skelter to the tree-tops and there in the knowledge of greater safety stayed to peer down between the leaves, silent and with startled eyes. A group of wildebeest, drinking on a sandbank backed by another fringe of trees, turned suddenly with one accord and raced through a narrow opening worn by themselves and other creatures amid thick undergrowth. Even the spotted kingfisher, swooping to catch fish beneath the hot surface of the river, darted away as the giant crocodile passed.

But he paid no attention to these creatures of the banks. At another time he might have lingered to secure food at one of the sandbanks, but now he was intent on establishing himself in a new home where he could live without undue trouble, where food would be plentiful and where there would be no more disturbance and danger like that from which he had just escaped. These sandbanks were small and unlikely to provide a constant supply of food for so large a creature as himself; nor had he yet found a spot where shade and the likelihood of small creeks piercing the banks suggested that he could live in comfort.

He swam and floated downstream through the heat of the day without resting. Then, towards evening, he came to a place where the river broadened into a deep oval pool, and he knew at once that his search was ended.

Here too was a sandbank, big and broad, with numerous tracks crossing it from the undergrowth and trees on its landward side to the water. Lower down the stream, on the further corner of the sandbank, a narrow channel, like a small backwater, ran up, dividing sand from solid earth. In that channel the crocodile would be able to lie, hidden by the water and shaded by the trees that lined its bank; thence he could come suddenly, rising between animals that stayed to drink from the river and the land to which they would try to escape. Cutting off that panic-stricken retreat, he would have easy hunting.

The opposite bank of the pool was heavily overhung with large trees, where, without doubt, he would find a creek, its entrance securely hidden in the shade and possibly so much overhung that no creature save himself would be able to find it.

At the upper end of the pool were small islands, some bare and rising a few feet above the surface, others thick with papyrus and giant palm, whose leaves cast shadows upon the water.

For him the place was ideal. There would be food in plenty, and thanks to that channel at the back of the sandbank the animals would remain unsuspicious of his presence and easy to catch. There was shade, whether he floated in sultry heat under the trees that lined the southern bank or kept close to a tree-covered island where the breeze would cross the pool. Under the trees on the bank he would find hollows where he could store his food, the roots entangling it and preventing it from drifting away. There would be a safe creek in which he could sleep, secure that no enemies could approach him, well shaded and perhaps by good fortune either broad or else surrounded by bare land, so that even with his immense length he would be able to turn within the confines of his home.

And more than all, as he discovered on that first inspection of the pool, there were other crocodiles already in possession, yet not too many; there were three, a male and two females of normal size, far smaller than himself, so that while he would have company and an end to loneliness, there would be no shortage in the abundant supplies which the sandbank suggested, and he with his greater speed and strength would have no rival in securing the best of anything that the pool might provide.

CHAPTER
FIVE

CROCODILE AND LEOPARD

ON the edge of a small island near the upper part of the pool, the crocodile passed the night, his jaws and the front part of his body resting on the shelving land, while his tail floated on the water. On the opposite side of the island lay a family of hippo, father, mother and youngster; and now and then a turtle would come as if painfully out of the water, cross the island, and slide back into the pool on the opposite side. But the crocodile paid no attention; he slept.

As the darkness deepened, the night awoke to vivid sound. From the distance, where the plain beyond the trees swept gradually upwards to the foot of the mountains, came occasionally the deep grunt-grunt of the lion seeking his prey. Thence, too, came the coughing of a leopard, the "boom, boom" of ostriches, the cry of jackals, and the anguished wail with which hyenas rend the night.

In the trees by the water's edge an owl called and monkeys—scared at some sound in the darkness—chattered. And once, close at hand, before morning broke, there came the deep-throated roar of a lion who had slaked his thirst after the kill.

But the crocodile did not stir, even at that last mighty sound, until the dawn broke, silhouetting the nearest hill against a sea of fleecy pink. Then at last he opened his eyes, lazily stretched his jaws, and moved backwards into the water.

He swam once slowly round the island, looking with interest at the hippo, who had returned from a night's feeding, and then he set off on a second voyage of exploration. At the edge of the sand-bank a group of impalla, slender and graceful, stood drinking. The crocodile, seeing them, drew silently near, submerged to the level of his eyes. He had not expected anything so fortunate yet, but such a chance was not to be missed. If the edge of the sandbank, which he had not yet explored, sloped suddenly under the water, he might be able to swim close enough to snap; if not—well, there would be nothing lost by the attempt, and later he would swim silently into the channel and win his prey by stealth.

But long before he was near enough for an attack he knew that it would be impossible, at least in daylight, for the sand sloped so gradually at the spot he was approaching that his body would be clear of the water while he was still several yards from the drinking animal; and even as he made that discovery, one of the impalla, suddenly raising her head, stared across the water in sudden terror, then turned and bounded away among the bushes, followed by the others.

The disappointment lasted but for a matter of minutes. He had at least learnt something about the way to approach that sandbank. Before the day was over he would have finished his exploring and would be ready to hunt by night, either by hiding in the channel or by snatching some animal from the end of the sandbank.

For an hour he swam lazily, round and round the pool, wondering on which of the small islands, or in which of the many narrow creeks that cut the banks, the crocodile family lived. Then, as the sun began to get hot and he regretted that the impalla had so easily escaped, he noticed a great unshapely mass floating out of the stream down which he had come the evening before.

43

He knew immediately that it was the body of a dead hippopotamus, distended by gas—a tasty dinner that could be eaten at once, without the troublesome delay which was necessary to provide a proper flavour to newly killed flesh. But even as he set off quickly towards it, a ripple spread on the surface to his left and another followed just behind; other crocodiles, the past owners and lords of the pool, were also hastening to the feast.

With the extra speed that came from his strength and size, the giant crocodile came first at the meat, closing his teeth on a piece of skin and tearing it away with a violent movement of his head from side to side. While his webbed feet moved in slow strokes to enable him to keep his position against the current, he strove for a larger mouthful; but by that time three further sets of powerful jaws were at work, each seeking a grip on the smooth surface of flesh. Two of the crocodiles quickly tore off substantial portions and swam away, leaving the youngest of the three still unsatisfied and the giant still determined that the whole of such a prize—or at least as much of it as yet remained—should be his.

The current carried the meat close in-shore,

THE SANDBANK—" here there would be food in plenty."

"The river broadened into a deep oval pool."

to a spot where a tree grew on the brink, one low bough overhanging the water within a few feet of the surface. Against the projecting root of this tree the body stopped, momentarily, and the crocodiles rejoiced at the greater ease thus given them for tearing it in pieces.

But even as the giant opened his jaws to their fullest width, he was disturbed by a soft sound from above. Paddling backwards, he looked up at the tree. There, lying at full length along the overhanging bough, was a leopard; and now the leopard's paw, reached down, was almost scraping the top of the floating meat.

Such interference was not to be borne. He would share the meal, if he must, with other crocodiles, though he was determined that his own share should be far larger than theirs; but he would not have a leopard, or any other creature of the land, helping himself to crocodiles' meat. He was enraged and he snapped at that hanging paw.

He missed it by inches, his upraised snout falling against the flank of the hippopotamus. The leopard, quick to profit by good fortune, stretched his long body more closely against the branch, the claws of one front paw firmly embedded in the bark, while the other strove again to reach the coveted meat. But at the same moment the giant crocodile, rearing himself out of the water, snapped again and his jaws closed on the tip of the leopard's paw, biting through skin and flesh and bone.

For a second the leopard rocked on the bough, as if he would be dragged downwards into the water. Then the crocodile slipped back, carrying with him half an inch of yellow fur, stained red.

The quietness of the morning was rent with a great growl of agony. While the two crocodiles nosed the meat away from the projecting root and then followed as the current bore it downstream towards some hollow where they could store it for use in future days, the leopard lay still along the branch, his tongue licking his wound.

CHAPTER
SIX

THE LEOPARD HUNTS

HE moved from the overhanging bough into
the shade of the trees, lying there and
licking uninterruptedly at his wound, until the
heat of the day had passed and it was cool enough
for him to start limping painfully homeward. He
passed through a thin belt of forest. There,
monkeys darted away, some to the tree-tops,
where they sat alert and ready to swing from
branch to branch should he spring into a tree,
others deeming distance their only safety and
going at once to further parts of the forest. Small
antelope, who also had spent the day in the shade,
sprang to their feet as he approached and hastened
away to safety.

Ordinarily at that hour the leopard would have
thought only of a kill; now he knew that he could
neither leap nor stalk—could do nothing in fact
but limp slowly and with much pain through the

forest and across the plain to the group of rocks among which he lived. Once a three-parts-grown monkey that had lingered behind and been cut off when the rest of its troop moved away seemed too tempting to be neglected; but as he crouched for a spring, digging his claws into the earth, the pain reminded him—more, it compelled him to rest again before he could continue his journey.

Once he had passed the forest-belt, things became a little easier, for the grass as he trod it was soft and free from the sticks and small stones which had previously hurt him. But his progress was slow and night had fallen before he reached the hill which was his castle. At the foot he stopped for a second to choose the easier of two paths that ran upward among the boulders, and near the top of the slope he let forth a long growl, which was a message of distress to his mate.

She, lying full length in the low cave with her two cubs beside her, got up suddenly and answered; a short, gruff growl of question and of assurance that she was there. Then she went to the entrance of the cave and stood looking down the side of the hill, expectantly, anxiously.

.   .   .   .   .

During the days that followed the leopard lay

48

in the cave where the cubs played like kittens, while his mate went out to hunt, returning with guinea-fowl, small buck or baboon. The wound healed slowly. At first the leopard made no attempt to move, except when he licked the paw or turned restlessly from side to side, or growled his annoyance when one of the cubs, tossing the foot of an impalla into the air and catching it, came too close. But within a week he was up, standing on the top of the hill, looking down into the valley and watching distant herds of antelope or gazelle which he knew he was not yet able to stalk.

Presently the cubs, growing apace, followed him and their mother to the edge of the crag and took their first look at the outside world. Overhead, vultures swooped, waiting till the coast should be clear so that they could seize the remains of a half-eaten impalla; one, passing low and with a sudden swirl over the rock, scared the cubs and made them crouch in fear—then rose, and the cubs, quickly bold again, stood to watch it circling. When they were bigger all fear of vultures would vanish and they would crouch catlike on the rock, in the hope that one would come too close; but now these swift creatures

D 49

that came suddenly from the sky were terrifying so that they had to run continually to their mother for protection.

The hill had one other inhabitant, an old rhino who lived among a clump of bushes a hundred yards away. The rhino and the leopard were neither friends nor enemies; they were neighbours with no interest in each other's affairs. Each kept to his own path down the side of the hill, the leopard picking his way gracefully among the stones, the rhino sliding down a slope of pebbly ground. They had, indeed, nothing in common except the neighbourhood of their homes. The leopard roamed afar for his prey, taking it where-ever he found it. The rhinoceros fed off the grass and vegetation of one tract of plain, approaching it always by the same path and leaving it by another to drink at the river—he was a creature of routine, while the leopard lived according to circumstance.

When at length the leopard set out again to seek his own food he started cautiously, but soon found that he could move without pain as long as he kept to flat stretches of grass: in the forest, or if he attempted to spring, it would doubtless be different, but that was a matter of the future;

first he must stalk the prey which he had seen afar off from the hill.

Moving lightly, he followed the direction he had marked in his mind's eye, leaving the wood and the river far on his right and turning towards the distant hills. In a little dell, a mile away, was a group of thorn trees under which as he knew a herd of gazelle occasionally sheltered; and there he had seen them as his eyes searched the plain that morning. Many a time he had taken toll there, just as, without doubt, he would kill to-day. Breasting a rise, he saw the trees ahead. The gazelle, closely grouped together, were grazing at its furthest corner; he would have to move so that the trees sheltered him and the wind took his scent away, where no animal could catch it and give the alarm.

Low in the grass, so that for the most part it covered his back, he moved stealthily, forgetful in his excitement of the pain that he had felt for a fortnight. His eyes singled out one male with beautifully curved horns—the nearest of the herd. When he reached the foot of the last tree he would spring. The animal showed no fear, nibbling contentedly at the short grass which it and the rest of the herd had shorn close

in a week of grazing. Now and then it would
sniff at the wind, as if in habit, without suspicion; then down once more would go its head,
to continue feeding. And minute by minute the
leopard drew nearer, up to the first of the trees,
past it, inch by inch, silent and with eyes that
never shifted from his prey.

At the foot of the last tree, trembling with
excitement, he gathered himself for his spring,
muscles taut, claws pressed hard on the earth,
body quivering and eyes steady; and then, as he
leapt forward, a sudden jab of pain shot through
his paw.

The stab brought his eyes for a fraction of a
second from the gazelle, and in that instant the
animal looked up and jumped. It had no time
to run before the leopard leapt—but it moved, in
sheer surprise, and that movement took it out of
reach of the spring and into safety. Then, in a
second, as the leopard landed where the gazelle
had stood an instant before, the whole herd took
to their heels, bounding away across the plain.

The leopard did not follow. Hunting for him
meant a stalk, with his prey ignorant of his
coming, or an ambush into which some unsuspicious thing might wander. Even at his best he

would not pursue an animal that had once escaped his spring; while now he knew that even stalking, with a wounded paw, was not to be done.

But just beyond the thorn trees one stouter tree grew, with a strong branch on which he had often lain in wait for animals to pass. Turning, he sprang upwards, ignoring the second jolt of pain that then ran up his leg. His claws fastened on the branch and he lay full length, chin on paws, waiting for what should come.

CHAPTER SEVEN

THE GRACEFUL IMPALLA

AS the day advanced, herds of antelope and gazelle made their way gradually towards the shelter of trees. Grazing as they came, a herd of forty zebra crossed the small plain, and a dozen impalla, headed by one old male, kept closely together just behind them. The zebra were stolid, keeping their noses to the ground, except for two of their number which kept pace with the herd a little distance on either side—sentinels, always maintaining a watch for danger. But the impalla took no precautions of their own, relying on the larger herd to give them warning. And though they fed steadily, they were light-hearted and frolicsome, playing together and leaping backwards and forwards as they came.

The youngest of the herd was but a few weeks old; she was extremely graceful, with her slender legs and neck, light-coloured markings, thin,

"The impalla was extremely graceful."

" She stayed on the sandbank to drink."

" An ugly shape, evil and horrible."

wide ears and finely pointed head. So young was she that the knowledge of danger had only come to her the day before when, with others of her herd, she had stayed on the sandbank to drink; and then, because of a sudden instinct, she had raised her head and looked across the pool. Out of the water an ugly shape was rising. It came relentlessly onwards with little gleaming eyes that looked evil and horrible. Terrified, she had bounded away, the other impalla close at her heels.

She did not know exactly what the danger had been, but she was quite sure that she would never dare to stay alone by the pool, and even with the others around her she would have constantly to look across the water lest strange and terrible things suddenly rose out of it. It was a pity, for there was little that was so pleasant, at the end of a warm day, as to put her nose to the water and linger there, the water seeming to spread a delightful coolness all through her body.

Life was good. It was good to nibble the short grass, to find quite suddenly a patch that was moister than the rest, to leap for fun with her brothers and sisters, to lie in the hottest hours at rest under the trees. Only by the pool were horrible things, but the memory of that ugly snout was so strong that it sometimes forced its way into pleasanter times, making her look up with a shudder from the grass, or even leap with a start from her sleep when she dreamt that she had not run away, but had stayed till the awful thing came close.

After a while the zebra turned to one side, moving towards a large clump of trees that grew close to the river; while the impalla kept on, in the direction of a number of thorn trees where they had often rested before in company with a small herd of gazelle. The shade there was good and the isolated position seemed to render it safe from sudden attack. The old male who was the leader of the herd saw that it was unoccupied, although the gazelle had not long left it; the grass was mostly grazed close, but that was of little account since it was for coolness and rest rather than for feeding that the clump was needed. He led the way under the trees and lay down, the others grouping themselves around him.

Some three hours later the young impalla awoke suddenly, with a strange sense of danger. Getting to her feet, she looked around, seeing the rest of the herd sleeping or resting undisturbed. One young male looked up as she moved, then rose and trotted towards her, standing for a minute with his head to hers and then trotting off to the edge of the clump. She followed, still troubled, though she had no idea what had awakened her nor what gave her this strange sense of fear. It was somehow akin to her feeling at the sight of the crocodile rising out of the water; an idea that she must run and run for miles and yet was unable to move. Curiosity held her, while fear urged her to go. But at least, this time, she was not alone. The impalla beside her was her friend, and from him she drew some feeling of safety.

A little distance from the clump one larger tree grew, with wide-spreading boughs. Towards this, the young ram moved, keeping a few paces ahead. He had no feeling of fear, only one of restlessness and of the desire to lead with the young doe following him. It was hot, too, and the shade was better under the larger tree; there they could rest together.

He moved into the shade. His young companion stopped for an instant to bite a little tuft of grass. She looked up quickly as she heard a sudden cry of fright, and then in the second before she ran she saw a great yellow form leaping on to the back of the ram, giant claws ripping his skin and bared teeth fastening themselves in his neck.

Inexpressible fear consumed her. She ran as she had never run before, not knowing where she went, not noticing that all the rest of the herd were flying together in the opposite direction. She had no thought but to move from that terrible vision of spotted fur, those teeth, and the little dying squeals of her friend.

It was long before she stopped running and looked behind her. No animal was in sight. There was nothing to be seen but the open plain, the mountains in the distance, and the belt of trees that marked the river. She thought then of the rest of the herd, wanting them, dreading the thought that she was alone. It was a world in which terrifying things rose out of water or leapt from trees, things which she didn't understand, but which she now knew meant death. And she had no friends beside her, to protect her or to teach her when she was safe and when in danger.

She stood for some minutes beset by that feeling of loneliness. Then, feeling the heat of the sun on her back, she turned in the direction of the trees, the nearest shade. Perhaps she would there find her friends; surely they too would have gone to the trees and she would find them grouped together, seeking the safety of companionship.

CHAPTER
EIGHT

AMONG THE BABOONS

THEY were not there. Without stopping to
graze, she roamed beneath the trees and
across patches of sunlight, searching everywhere
for her friends. There were animals in plenty,
but not her own kind. In the sparse shade of
three thin thorn trees sheltered a herd of wildebeest; close to them, where the shade was
stronger, were some fifty zebra, a few kongoni
and some gazelle; half-hidden behind thorn trees,
four giraffe nibbled at the upper leaves; and under
one tree, keeping its benefit to himself, stood an
old rhinoceros.

Among the many animals there gathered into
a small space the impalla was lonely. Feelings of
panic still stirred her, so that she started at the
slightest sound. She had no reason to be afraid of
any of these creatures, for they paid no attention
to her and felt no interest in her; but if a wilde-

beest snorted she turned to run, and when a restless gazelle got suddenly to its feet she imagined that something was about to spring on her. But for the most part she thought only of finding the rest of her herd. She came once upon unmistakable signs that impalla had recently passed that way, and she set off quickly along the trail. She was overjoyed when she came upon them, grazing quietly under the trees, but then she found that these were strangers—her own species, it is true, but not the friends for whom she was searching. For a while she lingered with them, hoping for recognition, but although two of them came to smell her they gave her no welcome, and indeed seemed as little interested in her as the zebra and the wildebeest had been. With them, too, she was a stranger, to be tolerated without interest while she did not interfere with the choicest patches of grass and the best pieces of shade, but not to be welcomed into the herd itself.

So after a while she left them and wandered on, her eyes and nose seeking signs in the grass that would give her the news she wanted. Presently she realised that she was very thirsty. Seeing a track that led towards the river she followed it, overtaking a herd of wildebeest with whom she mixed, still a stranger amongst twenty animals that were accustomed to live together. Other tracks ran among trees and bushes in the same direction, and down them came ostriches, kongoni, gazelle and water-buck. Presently the tracks converged into a single broad pathway, where a herd of elephants, moving very slowly and investigating everything with their trunks as they went, blocked the road. A great bull elephant led, cows and calves followed, and the other animals soon pressed close behind, eager to get to the water but afraid to come forward while the elephants were there.

Where the track emerged from the bushes and divided into innumerable small paths across the sandbank to the river, the elephants stopped to gather sand in their trunks and blow it over their backs; and the smaller animals waited with impatience till they should have finished. The impalla passed to the left of the elephants, some of whom were now sluicing themselves with water, and made alone for the opposite end of the sandbank; but as she reached a clear view of the river the memory came to her of a former occasion when she had gone to drink, and she looked fearfully towards the opposite bank, expecting to see again that grim snout and those small staring eyes.

But the surface of the water was still, save for the ripples made by the elephants as they drank; and that gave her confidence, so that she could almost have believed that she had never really seen the horror that she so clearly remembered. Gingerly she put her nose down to the water and drank.

She felt greatly refreshed by the time she turned away, and greatly comforted by the fact that nothing terrible had happened. Every minute she had expected to see those set eyes at the level of the water. But all had remained still. She had been able to drink her fill and then to walk quietly back through the skirting of bushes to the first of the trees.

Yet although she now felt calmer and less expectant of danger, she realised that she was still utterly alone. From herd to herd she went, unmolested but unwelcomed. She was virtually an outcast, and homeless; and the thought of the night, with its added dangers, made her long more than ever for the comforting presence of her own herd.

In a glade that crossed a stretch of wooded country she stopped for a moment to graze. Baboons were resting under the trees, the youngsters playing, the mothers watching, the old male who was their leader sitting on a high branch alert as a sentinel. Among the bushes at the edge of the wood, something moved stealthily; but the impalla's back was towards it and she went on feeding, quite unaware of the cheetah that crouched, his eyes fastened on her as he began to creep closer. Then suddenly the watchful old baboon saw a glint of brownish-yellow move behind a bush fifty yards away and he called out—the quick bark with which the baboons tell of urgent danger. The youngest baboons chattered with fright and hustled to the sides of their mothers, jumping up and clinging to their breasts; the leader and the other males stood at bay, with teeth bared. And the young impalla leapt forward, out of danger.

She ran, instinctively, among the baboons and there stood, just behind a bush, her limbs shaking, ready to run further if necessary. The cheetah came a few steps nearer and then stopped, hesitating at the sight of the six big baboons who he knew would fight desperately if he came within their reach. Then, because he could no longer see the impalla and because he felt that in any case she was not worth so much trouble when easier prey was doubtless to be found elsewhere, he turned and went back into the bushes.

The clamour of shouting baboons continued for several minutes. Then the leader of the troop gave the shout which means "all clear," the mothers set down their babies, the youngsters began playing again, and the males, gathering in a group at the foot of a tree, started chattering together as if in argument.

The young impalla did not move away. She knew that she had been in great danger and that the cheetah would undoubtedly have caught her but for the warning given by the baboon. That warning was the first sign of interest that any creature had showed in her since she had left her own herd, and already she felt that the baboons were her friends. They would not merely allow her to be amongst them, but would warn her when she was in danger, would even fight for her. She could stay with them, in safety at last and no longer with the feeling of loneliness.

In the middle of the troop she stood grazing. The argument between the baboons had developed until it threatened to end in a fight, but just as the first blow was struck, the old leader clambered down from the tree on which he was sitting and came to settle the quarrel. At the sight of him, the others scattered, jumping into trees, and then, when he retired, coming down and starting to play together, the dispute entirely forgotten.

Suddenly the leader, again on the look-out, gave a short bark, different from the shout with which he had warned the troop before but a sign nevertheless that all was not as it should be. The baboons, undecided what was the trouble, stood for a minute on the alert; then another signal from the leader told them that the danger had passed. Then the leader, descending from his tree, called to the troop to move. Mothers cuddled their small babies, bigger youngsters climbed on to the hind-quarters of their mothers for a ride, and all moved off down the glade, stopping as they went to gather small bulbs and plants from the earth or to turn over stones in the hope of finding insects or scorpions beneath them.

The impalla kept pace with them, feeling a security which she had not known all day. She had quenched her thirst and satisfied her hunger, and now she had found safety. As long as she stayed with the baboons, all would be well.

At a little distance on the further side of the glade, stood a tall rock, rising in a series of sheer cliffs on one side but sloping more gradually on the further side, where the rock was partially covered with earth and grass. There the baboons had their home, living in a number of little caves in the rocky face. As they came to it, the baboons bounded up the cliffs, from spur to spur, and the impalla, left alone at the foot, felt herself once more alone, for she could not jump as they could. But she did not want to be deprived of this newly found companionship and she walked around the foot of the rocky hill, seeking some way of climbing it. When she came to the further side, she ascended the slope and was able at last to step on to a flat ledge a few feet from the top. There she lay down, rejoicing in the knowledge that four of the baboons were at her side, while others could be heard chattering in a cave close by.

Night fell and she slept. She awoke suddenly as one of the baboons cried out and instantly there was pandemonium on the rock, the whole troop shouting, barking and shrieking. She did not know what had happened, but she felt fear and pressed herself very flat against the surface of the rock on which she lay. And then, on the ground at the foot of the hill, the moonlight gave her a sudden glimpse of the dreaded yellow form of a leopard, carrying the body of a half-grown baboon in its teeth.

CHAPTER
NINE

THE FIRE

THE night was very cold. When morning came the baboons gathered on the cliffs of the rock face so that the sun might give them warmth. They were quiet at first, half-frozen, but after a while as the heat increased, some of the younger ones began to play a game, pushing each other off a small rock and scrambling back, in turn to push or to be pushed off once more. The older baboons too became more active as they grew warmer; the leader had once again taken up his position as sentinel, and now two of the other males were stationed on headlands of the rock, watching the valley below and the grassy slope behind. Since the coming of the leopard in the night there was an air of unrest upon the rock. The mothers chattered and grunted more than they would normally have done and took greater care of their youngsters. When one was pushed off the lowest step of the rock and went to look for fruit on a tree instead of at once climbing back, his mother sprang agitatedly down the rock to fetch him; and the preliminary signal of danger was given with a frequency which showed that the nerves of the sentinels were on edge.

The impalla also was cold when she awoke; and she too remembered with horror that cry in the night and what had caused it. As she lay on her shelf of rock she realised that it was from the cave close by that the young baboon had been stolen. Its mother was sitting on the edge of the rock, her hands drooping between her knees, her attitude so fixed that even when the alarm was given she did not stir. And when at last the leader called to the troop to leave the rocks and set out on a foraging expedition which would bring them eventually to the river, she was the last to move.

When the baboons clambered down the rocks, skirting the base of the hill and continuing among the bushes, scattered rocks and occasional trees amongst which they would find their food, the impalla left the rock also by the way she had come, soon overtaking the baboons and grazing in the midst of them. The old leader still showed

70

" His eyes fastened on her as he began to creep closer."

BABOONS—" The males chattered as if in argument."

" The old leader would climb a tree."

even greater caution than usual. Marching a little ahead of the rest, again and again he would climb a tree to scan the ground ahead, then climb down, continue for a short distance and climb once again, whilst on either side of the troop other sentinels did the same. And when, towards midday, the troop went to the river to drink, he still kept watch, for even the impalla, nervously drinking beside him, did not dread the crocodiles more than did the baboons.

Yet that day nothing happened. Twice, as the animals drank, the sharp, urgent warning was given, so that youngsters grabbed at their mothers, one darted in terror up a thorn tree, and the impalla stood petrified with fear. But each time the "all clear" quickly followed as the water rippled in the wake of retreating crocodiles.

The impalla was resting in the heat of the following afternoon, while zebra, kongoni, wildebeest and gazelle, their sentries on the look-out at a little distance, stood or lay under the trees close by. The baboons sheltered among the dry leaves of the trees, even the youngsters finding it too hot to play. Suddenly the sentinel of the wildebeest lifted his head and stood sniffing the air. The animals nearest to him, taking the alarm

71

immediately, raised their heads and stood expectant. Other herds took up the news; some of the baboons climbed down from the trees and stood hesitating; the young impalla got hurriedly to her feet; all eyes were turned in the one direction as, over the top of a slight rise, a wreath of smoke appeared.

No one waited then. Zebra, kongoni, wildebeest and gazelle turned and trotted off, away from the fire, the baboons made for their home, and the impalla, very anxious not to be left alone in face of a mysterious danger that was new to her, went with the baboons.

But although the baboons could clamber up and sit in their caves, the ledge on which the impalla had passed the previous night now met the full heat of midday, and after a single look at it she turned and bolted down again to the foot of the rocky hill. There, a huge boulder which must have fallen from the crag many years before seemed to provide security; behind it she lay down, pressing herself flat on the earth from a feeling that only so might she escape the notice of this strange new enemy which now threatened her. For to the young impalla, as she peeped nervously from behind the rock, the fire appeared to be a living thing, and very terrifying.

Never had she seen anything resembling it. By now it had spread and was sweeping forward over a stretch of ground nearly a mile wide, the dry grass crackling in flames which rose here and there to a height of a dozen feet. Smoke, moved by the steady breeze, advanced like a dense curtain overhead. The fire was relentless, coming ever nearer, and devouring the two-foot-high grass until nothing was left but little bits of charred stubble.

As she realised how certainly it was advancing and how it must soon reach the rocks amongst which she lay, she wished that she had not stayed with the baboons, but had fled with the zebra and the wildebeest. But when she half rose, deciding even now to save herself by running, she found that a belt of flame had pressed forward to her left and was already licking the edge of the rocks, while to the right the same thing had happened. Only immediately in front of her, where the ground was stony, with many small, fallen boulders, had the flames been checked.

As she stood there uncertainly, doubtful whether to try to run past the edge of the fire, close to

the rocks, or to stay where she was, a cheetah
leapt down from the rocks some distance away.
Instinctively she crouched back to lie hidden
among the boulders, so that the cheetah did not
see her in his hurry to escape from the fire and
the smoke. In great bounds he galloped across
the nearest tongues of flame and made off towards
the river. Then a python swept past, at great
speed, and disappeared down a deep crack
between two of the rocks. Two small dik-dik,
driven out of the grass, came into the stony patch,
looked at the line of high rocks which they could
not climb, ran back, met again the advancing
flames, and then ran desperately round and round,
too frightened to notice the one small passage,
close to the rocks, through which they might
even then have escaped.

Into the patch of stones in front of the
impalla's refuge two streams of fire advanced,
burning small clumps of dry grass and soon
uniting to make a new line of moving fire. Then
the flame caught a taller clump and leapt to a
great height, blackening the rocks. The baboons
cried out in terror. Youngsters clasped their
mothers, the males with teeth half-bared faced a
danger which no tooth nor claw could fight.

74

" A cheetah leapt down from the rocks."

" The fire was sweeping forward."

" The thunder of the hoofs of stampeding animals."

The impalla pressed backward behind the sheltering boulder till she could go no further and lay gasping, her eyes widely staring, her mouth open, her heart beating wildly.

From the valley below came again and again the thunder of the hoofs of stampeding animals. The frantic shouts of the baboons mixed with the crackling of the flames, and once was heard the deep, angry growl of a lion.

But as time passed the flames died down. Here and there were lines of grey and white, tree-shaped, where a fallen tree had burnt away, leaving an outline of itself in ashes; and now and again one of these, fanned by the wind, would suddenly burst into flame. But such unsupported fires soon died. The danger here had passed, although beyond the hill the flames still swept on, burning fiercely, moving forward and leaving a charred road behind them.

As the air grew cooler the young impalla hesitatingly moved forward till she could see into the open country beyond the boulder. She saw the black rings among the stones where the fire had almost crossed the bare zone and reached the foot of the hill, and beyond, a great blackened stretch, a mile in width, with short brown grass

75

on either side of it, to mark the track of de-
vastation. She saw the two little dik-dik suddenly
stop circling as they realised that the danger was
over and dash together across the charred ground
towards the distant grass; and she knew that she
too was now safe.

Yet she did not immediately move; and as she
waited, from a hill not far to her right came a
family of lions. Even they, who were lords of the
forest and had little to fear from any other
creature, were terrified at this devastating enemy
who swept on and on, checked here and there by
stones, but always advancing—an enemy whom
even a lion could not attack. Once, long before,
the lion, then a cub, had leapt to tear with teeth
and claws at the flames on a small burning patch
of grass; he had found nothing that his claws
could touch, but he had felt great pain. That
memory had lasted. As he grew bigger, he never
stayed again to face advancing fire but galloped
for shelter, filled with terror at the sight and
sound of tearing, leaping, crackling flame. So
now, while he had been crawling through long
grass, half playfully stalking a buck, he had seen
the fire rising above a hill; and without a
moment's delay he had sought his mate and had

led her and the cubs to the shelter of rocks. There they had crouched until now he could lead them away, past the foot of the blackened hill and across the plain to his lair.

At the sight of them, as they emerged, the leader of the baboons cried out his urgent alarm, and the frantic shouting recommenced. But the lions paid no attention. They would kill baboons at any other time, just as they would kill impalla; but now they were in haste to get home, away from the fire which was still sweeping across the open country on the further side of the hill.

For an hour after their going the impalla lay in her shelter, waiting expectantly for fresh alarms. But nothing happened. The fire swept on, to die out when the wind dropped at nightfall. The hot earth cooled. Small snakes came from holes in the earth into which they had crept, animals appeared from many small gaps and crevices among the rocks and started, as the two dik-dik had already done, to make their way back to the unburnt grass. The baboons quieted down. And then at last the impalla came from behind her boulder and stood for a while looking out at the strange, burnt land.

CHAPTER TEN

THE LION CUBS

IT had all seemed very sudden and surprising to the two lion-cubs, and they could not even yet make out what had happened. They had been playing on the grass some distance from their lair, close beside their mother, when suddenly their father had come and his excited purr had brought the lioness instantly to her feet. Then they had been hustled along, much faster than they could comfortably move, towards a big heap of rocks. Their mother had nosed them into a small cave, making them stay at the far end of it where the roof was so low that they could hardly stand upright. She had lain down in front of them, and when, full of curiosity, they had in turn scrambled on to each other's back, they had been able to see that their father was crouching in the entrance, his back quivering with excitement.

Then still stranger things had happened. The air had suddenly become stiflingly hot and very difficult to breathe, so that they coughed and choked; and from outside had come a crackling, snapping noise. When they choked, their first idea had been to run outside into the open to get away from the smoke which filled the cave. But when the smaller of the two had tried to leap across his mother's legs, she had turned and growled at him in a way which he knew meant that he must not try to do that again; and when, a little later, because the choking and the coughing and the heat seemed unbearable, he *had* tried again to get past and out of the cave, she had struck him with her paw.

After that the two cubs had pressed their noses close against their mother's skin, becoming frightened as well as uncomfortable as they heard their father's low angry growl and felt the cave growing hotter and hotter. Once a puff of hot wind came into the cave, blowing out the smoke, and the smaller cub, standing up for a minute with his front paws against his mother's back, saw the outside world above his father's head— and it had become amazingly red and yellow, moving and dancing, and crossed with clouds of

79

thick, grey smoke. Then the wind came again, bringing the smoke again into the cave, and the cub jumped quickly down, coughing, to press his mouth into a little safe corner between his brother's body and his mother's back.

They had lain there for some time before they realised that the air was at last becoming clearer; and presently their mother got to her feet, went forward to the mouth of the cave and lay down just behind their father. Then a few minutes later he rose to his feet and the cubs knew that it was time to move.

Keeping close behind their mother they came to the entrance. What they saw was astonishing. The ground was no longer brown and soft, with tall waving grass, but black and stubbly. It was all black as far as they could see, and even the rock was marked with black streaks. Indeed, before they had travelled far, much of the blackness covered their own legs and faces. But they were not given time to think of that nor to wonder what could have happened. Their father was already ahead and their mother, now just at their heels, was continually pressing them onward with her nose. Sometimes she turned aside to sniff at the air and then hurried on, past the cubs,

80

and then, as if suddenly remembering them, came back again to hurry them on. The smaller cub found it impossible to go so fast and after a while his mother put her teeth to the back of his neck, picked him up and carried him. But he did not like that kind of thing, being several weeks old; although not quite so big or strong as his brother, he had lately grown very rapidly. So after a few yards his mother set him down and began again urging him to run; and then, once more looking anxiously behind her, she picked him up and carried him for another thirty yards.

He was very glad when at last they came back to the bushy ravine in which they had their lair. There, where the undergrowth grew thickest, the bushes and branches had been trampled and pushed aside into a tunnel which broadened as it ran back. Trees grew overhead, their branches giving an added protection from sun and rain, and the nearest wall of the ravine formed one side of the home, the interwoven bushes and undergrowth making the opposite wall and a roof.

In the safety of their own domain the lions turned and lay down on the grass just above the ravine. The cubs lay panting with exhaustion; the lioness kept watchfully close to them; and every now and again the lion got to his feet and stood looking back across the way they had come, to the hill of rock which could still be seen against the skyline.

The cubs were tired. For long hours they lay sleeping, but by the morning the fatigue had worn off and youthful spirits revived. Then on the open ground at the edge of the ravine the smaller of the two chased his brother in a circle, of which their mother was the centre, twisting and dodging, jumping clumsily about, pulling up short as the pursued suddenly turned to face his pursuer, exchanging a few friendly blows of the paw, then off again, each chasing the other in turn. When the excitement of the game took them further along the ravine so that they were out of sight of home, their mother quickly came to look for them, driving them before her until they were back near the mouth of the tunnel, and then lying down majestically while they continued to circle round her.

Their father, who had gone out in the early morning, now returned. For an hour he had stalked a herd of kongoni, not very seriously because the day was not the time for serious hunting, but always with a view to the possi-

bility that what had been begun as a game might
luckily turn into business; and this time that had
happened, for when the outlying sentinels had
seen him as he crept through the long grass and
the herd had bounded away, one old kongoni
which had grazed apart from the others had
stayed too long before rejoining the herd, so that
he had been able to stalk and kill it. It was not
often that anything so fortunate happened in broad
daylight, but chances of that kind were not to be
thrown away, and after eating what he could of
the kill he dragged the remainder back to his
mate and the cubs.

They devoured this surprise meal as greedily
as if food had been a rarity, the lioness crouching
over the kill, tearing off a chunk of flesh, holding
it down with her claws while she repeatedly drew
her rough tongue across it before settling down
to eat, then rising and walking round the carcase
in search of another dainty piece; and the cubs
each taking a smaller portion, carrying it a yard
or two away and then lying down to deal with it
exactly as their mother did with hers.

High overhead, vultures soared, waiting till
the remains of the meal should be left. Again and
again one more daring than the rest would swoop

down and sail low over the kill, then rise again to swoop once more. When the lions' meal was finished and the lioness slept, the vultures became still bolder, hovering lower in the air and swooping more frequently; but none dared to land while the lions were still at home.

The lion, pleased with his work and unusually well fed, came closer to the cubs and started to play with them. Grasping the smaller one in his paws he rolled over on to his back, then he let it drop gently on one side of him, rolled back, picked up the other, and then turned again to meet the first which by then was climbing across his shoulders. He sparred with his cubs, striking them playfully and receiving from them little buffets in return. Meanwhile, the lioness awoke, lay for a while watching her mate and the cubs, and then, tiring of that, turned over to look up at the vultures. Her eyes followed their swift flight as they circled and planed down, climbed back to a height, and descended once more. Lazily she wished, as she had so often wished before, that one would come yet lower, so that she could grasp it as it passed; but that never happened: it was only an idle but pleasurable dream.

During the heat of the day they all slept under the shade of a tree. Soon evening came. The lion restlessly got to his feet and stood looking across the plain, but his mate did not move. There was no need to hunt to-night, after that satisfying meal of kongoni, and it was good to lie lazily, half dreaming, while the cubs continued to sleep. But as night deepened, the mother rose at last, woke the two cubs and shepherded them into the lair where they could sleep in safety.

Then she and the still restless lion moved towards the river. If another chance of a kill came they would certainly take it, though they felt no hunger. But they must drink. On the way they stalked a herd of eland until the sentinels suspected their presence and gave the alarm. That did not matter. They had found pleasure in the stalk, and on another night they would be more successful.

They reached the river and drank, and then returned to the lair.

The lion's half-playful stalking the next day was fruitless, the sentinels of herds twice giving the alarm before he was near enough to spring. He felt disappointment then, for once he had been certain that his approach was unsuspected.

But these stalks of the daytime were unimportant; in the night he and his mate would hunt once more, and then without doubt they would kill.

As the evening drew near his restlessness returned, and now the lioness shared it. Food must be provided that night, for the cubs as well as for herself. So as darkness fell, the lion and lioness again led their cubs to the lair, leaving them to sleep, side by side, cosily snuggling together.

THE LION.

" The lion restlessly got to his feet."

CHAPTER ELEVEN

LIONS HUNT BY NIGHT

LEAVING their cubs in the lair, the lion and
the lioness set out across the plain. They
went first to a little dip in the ground where water
collected from the rains; it was not very far from
their home, and although in this season it would
have almost dried up so that there was no
great chance that animals would use it for
drinking, it was easy for the lions to seek their
kill there first and then if necessary go on towards
the river. When they were two hundred yards
from the dip, they sank into the grass and then
moved inch by inch without raising themselves,
so that the grass covered their backs.

Step by step they went forward, the lion a
few paces ahead of the lioness, but never directly
in front of her. They moved so slowly and
cautiously that the blades of the grass only stirred
faintly, with little more movement than might

have been caused by the breeze. Then, when they had but another fifty yards to cover, the lion stopped and the lioness moved up alongside him.

The dip was nearly bare of water and the earth was churned with the footmarks of many animals. From what little water there was, an eland was drinking—a fine creature, nearly six feet high, with beautiful, partly spiral horns. He was very nervous. Every minute he stopped drinking to raise his head and peer into the dusk, turning to look first on one side and then on the other, and every now and again turning completely round to make sure that no enemy could approach unsuspected behind him. Suddenly, while his head was down to drink, he started; and at the same moment the lion and lioness began with infinite caution to creep forward once more till they should be close enough to spring.

But it was not of them that the eland was suspicious. His keen ears had heard a sound afar off which gradually neared the pool. He did not wait to see what it was. With a bound and a whisk of his tail, he was off, leaving the pool between himself and the lions.

As he went, the lion and lioness sank again

88

into the grass and lay still, watching. They too had now heard the approaching sound, and a minute or two later two rhinoceros came into sight. The direction of the wind prevented them from getting the lions' scent and they passed on with a false sense of security. They were peaceable creatures with small interests beyond their feeding, a drink at a pool or at the river, and a refreshing bath in cool mud.

It was for the pleasures of a bath that they had now come down to this half-emptied pool—for that and to drink. They drank first, and then lay rolling and wallowing in the mud at the edge of the water, till a damp reddish covering was smeared over the greater part of their bodies. Then they rose—and suddenly began to play. Heavily, lumberingly, they chased one another round and round the little pool, puffing and squealing with excitement as they went. They were thoroughly enjoying themselves, without fears and without cares.

The lion and the lioness did not stay after the coming of the rhinos. That pool was no longer of any interest for them, since they did not want to attack the two rhinoceros and no gazelle or zebra were likely to visit the dip that night.

Turning, they stood up and walked away, in the direction of the river.

They crossed a stretch of open country, passed under several thorn trees in which monkeys sheltered, scared a group of giraffe, and came to the beginning of the thick undergrowth and bushes that bordered the river. A quarter of a mile away, as they knew, was the first of the paths that led to the sandbank; and it was towards that that they turned. The lioness went straight, just beyond the bushes; the lion turned aside, in among the close-growing clumps, and then keeping parallel with his mate along the bank of the river. A hundred yards from the path the lioness sank close to the ground and then crept onward.

Presently a small herd of zebra came across the plain. The darkness was increasing, and it was impossible for the animals to tell that the lioness lay waiting in the long grass, eighty yards away. They came on hurriedly, a sentinel leading with eyes and nose alert. At the outskirts of the thicker country the sentinel stopped, and then, satisfied that all was well, he advanced again, the others following in a compact group.

As they disappeared along the path among the

" The lion stood looking back across the way they had come."

" His excited purr brought the lioness to her feet."

bushes, the lioness crept slowly and cautiously forward until she lay close enough to the path to be able to spring on any animal that came by it. If another herd came to drink she would intercept them; but she was not thinking of that. One of the zebra who had already passed would be her prey—soon they would gallop in panic back along the path, and then she would pounce.

The zebra went on, unsuspecting that the road was closed behind them. Soon they could see small patches of sky and water through the trees lining the river ahead; a few more steps would bring them out on to the sandbank. And then suddenly the terrifying *grunt—grunt—grunt* of the lion pierced the night. His head was level with the ground and the sound travelled strangely, seeming to come now from one position, now from another.

The zebra, hesitating for a second, could not tell whether it came from the right or the left or straight ahead. But it filled them with terror and they turned with one accord, racing back along the path. And then, when one of them had all but reached the open grass, a yellow streak seemed to flash through the air as the lioness leapt from her ambush. She landed on a zebra's back, one set of claws gripping its shoulder and the other at its nose, forcing the head back and back, while her teeth sank deep into the back of its neck. And as she bit she gave a rumbling growl.

The zebra's front legs suddenly sagged beneath it; it fell dead across the path. And the rest of the herd, shying and swinging to the left, dashed past in terror.

In a minute the lion had joined his mate at the kill, giving a low crooning sound as he lay down, lapping the warm blood and then tearing at the flesh. In her excitement the lioness growled at him when he came too close to her.

For an hour they lay there, feeding on the kill. Out of the darkness behind them jackals and hyenas crept, to wait their turn at a little distance; and when at last the feast was finished and the lions moved away towards the river, the hyenas slipped forward to scavenge, whilst the jackals still circled round, afraid to come nearer but ever hopeful of snatching titbits.

The lion and lioness, now comfortably fed, went down to the river to slake their thirst. At the edge of the sandbank the lion stopped and gave his great, triumphant, full-throated roar, repeated again and again, growing in volume and then gradually dying away, that all the animals who heard it might know that once again the lions had killed. And at the sound, animals coming to drink turned back in fear.

Yet the lion and lioness, for all their triumph, became suddenly cautious as they neared the water. On the land they were all-powerful and every animal gave place to them; but in the river, as they knew, were creatures who had no fear of them, who might if they chose seize them as they drank and drag them beneath the surface. Before then they had seen dark, evil shapes rising from the river and they had drawn back, afraid to drink. So now, where the water lapped the sand, they stood hesitating, no longer triumphant and unassailable, but filled with a strange fear of what might come from the darkness. At last, gingerly and with suspicion, they lowered their heads and drank. And then, with their thirst quenched, they turned away, becoming once again bold and terror-striking lords of the jungle; and once again they sent abroad their awful challenging roar of triumph.

CHAPTER
TWELVE

CROCODILES IN THE CREEK

THE lion's triumphant roar echoed back across the river from the trees on its opposite bank. At the sound, two hippo, feeding on the grass just beyond those trees, looked up and turned their heads in the direction of the sandbank, and then quietly slipped back into the greater safety of the river; cormorants and vultures awoke from sleep; monkeys on the further bank moved restlessly, for all that the breadth of the river lay between them and the danger. All the creatures of the river and the river-bank were disturbed and anxious—all, except the crocodiles in the shallow water of creeks, who only opened their watery eyes, stirred and lay for a while sleepily gazing across the river.

In the few days since his arrival at the pool the giant crocodile had settled down to a life of comfort and successful hunting.

94

After the wounded leopard had crawled from the branch, the current had soon carried the dead hippopotamus downstream and the giant crocodile, eagerly following it, had found the young female still beside him. He did not mind that. He had resented the coming of three crocodiles to share his feast, yet he felt differently towards one alone, and ready, even, to welcome her companionship. He let her help in dragging the lump of meat below the surface to a deep hollow in the bank, where the exposed roots of an overhanging tree prevented the current from sweeping it away; and when, as they swam together towards the lower end of the pool, she turned aside to enter a narrow creek, he followed her.

When he had swum round the pool at his first coming to it he had not seen that creek, so thick were the vines that hung entangled across its entrance. And even now, as he swam close behind the tail of his mate, his greater breadth compelled him in places to force a new passage for himself. Yet inside, behind that veiled entrance, was a pool, dark and shadowed by trees, but broad enough for him to be able to turn in it. Tall papyrus and palm trees grew close to its banks, vines and undergrowth trailed down to the water; a long narrow shelf of mud, in this season just clear of the surface, lay along one side of it. It was a dark backwater, stagnant and still, except when his movement or that of his mate stirred it and caused a muddy sediment to rise and ripple against the banks.

In that creek the two crocodiles made their home. There was water for swimming, a shelf on which they could rest; it was hidden and dark and safe. A finer home for crocodiles could not easily be found.

Moreover, the neighbouring sandbank proved to be an easy hunting-ground, where sufficient meat could be secured even to satisfy the giant's flesh-eating appetite. In the channel of water that ran in at one side, close to where earth and sand were joined, the crocodiles could swim. They would lie with only their eyes and nostrils above the surface while animals came from under the trees and crossed the sandbank to drink from the pool. Then they would rise and run forward at great speed. At the sound zebra or gazelle would turn terror-stricken and race back from the shore; but often there would be no time to move, or else an animal would be intercepted by one of the crocodiles; then jaws would suddenly open and snap, and the victim would be caught by head or leg. Or else a crocodile, instead of snapping, would suddenly swing round, the great tail sweeping like a weighted scythe and knocking the animal to the ground, where he would be speedily seized and dragged to drown in the pool.

Sometimes a cautious buck, experienced and well aware of the danger, would hesitate before crossing the sand as he approached the river at twilight. While he waited there, his eyes searching the darkness, one or other of the crocodiles would move; or else the moon, coming suddenly from behind a cloud, would glint upon the water, showing a patch of jagged black amid the silver. Then, with a little nervous jump, the buck would turn and run, and all other animals approaching the sandbank would catch the message of fear and go back or stand waiting. Only after an hour of quietness, while the crocodiles lay, half-submerged, without movement, some bolder gazelle would go forward, the other animals moving very shyly behind him. He would advance a dozen steps, stand to listen and watch, go forward again, stop again, reach the beginning of the sandbank, peer into the channel of water where the crocodiles waited, now almost entirely under the water, and then at last step gingerly forward across the sand to drink. And then, before the other animals could join him, one of the two crocodiles, impatient after a tedious wait, would move and begin to come from the water; and the gazelle, taking the alarm at that first slight movement, would run back, reaching safety a second before the crocodile could get near enough to snap.

But even then, after another hour of waiting, a thirsty animal would again venture forward, and the crocodiles would be rewarded for their patience. They did not come to the sandbank every night, but when they came they usually took toll, sometimes early, sometimes late. If the lions had hunted in the direction of the river, the sandbank would afterwards be deserted for several hours; but eventually thirst would prove more compelling than fear and then the crocodiles would have their opportunity. Though the sandbank might for a time seem a terror-ridden spot, it was essential to the life of the many animals living in that part of the valley, and sooner or later another carcase would be dragged under water to the hollows below the bank, and the

98

two crocodiles would return, well satisfied, to
their shadowed creek.

.   .   .   .   .

There they lived in contentment for several
weeks. They hunted, slept, ate from their larder,
explored the pool, chased and caught large fish,
or visited a low island of rock on which they
rested and sunned themselves.

That island was the visiting-place also of a
family of hippo, of cranes, of herons and of water-
turtles. The hippo would feed during the night
on the grass of the further bank, but their home
was the water of the pool, where they would
lazily swim and float, sometimes sinking beneath
the surface, bobbing up, blowing a shower of
spray into the air, then sinking again; and
through the heat of the day they would come to
the island, there to lie basking inertly in the sun-
shine. The cranes and herons would stand for
hours on the sand that thinly covered the rock,
kingfishers would hover over the pool, and when
the crocodiles came to lie half on the island half
in the water, plovers would alight beside them
and act as vermin-catchers when they opened
their jaws.

Save for the creek, that island was the only place

where the coming of the crocodiles did not cause terror. The hippo mothers would guard their small youngsters, but otherwise the scene was one of perfect peace between birds and beasts. It was a place where the heat of the sun forbade activity, crocodile and hippo alike remaining immovable, the water-turtles creeping slowly past, the herons standing like statues, the cranes, apparently one-legged, only moving to change one leg for the other.

To that island would come also the other crocodiles of the pool. They had not welcomed the coming of the giant who so far outmatched them in speed and strength that he was always the first to reach anything eatable which occasionally floated down the stream—the rare but easily acquired prizes of their life. If any smaller crocodile had arrived from other parts of the river and had attempted to dispute their rights in the pool they would have fought him, either killing him or driving him away. But the enormity of the giant filled them with fear, so that they suffered his presence without protest. They did not attempt to hunt at the sandbank when he was there. While he and his mate were in their creek the other two crocodiles, when fish did not satisfy them, would visit the channel behind the sandbank and secure their prey; but while the giant hunted they lay at a distance, in their own creek or in the water on the further side of the pool.

The island was the one piece of common ground to which all the creatures of the pool might come. There the approach of the giant would cause no disturbance; there was room for all on its shores, and the overpowering heat was master, drowsiness taking the place of antagonism.

The giant lived easily in these surroundings. In the shelter of the creek he would lie lazily beside his mate on the long shelf or occasionally walk with a slow swinging gait on to the land just within the circle of giant palms and papyrus. The creek and the pool became the centre of his life. He forgot his old home further up the river and the two crocodiles with whom he had previously hunted; he forgot the encounter with men that followed the building of the bridge; he forgot his long journey down the stream. He was no longer alone, no longer beset by dangers; he was well fed and entirely at ease. He had no idea that such peaceful conditions would not last for ever.

CHAPTER
THIRTEEN

IMPALLA AND ZEBRA

WHEN at last the fire had passed on and even the ashes of trees had ceased to glow, the young impalla came out from behind the boulder at the foot of the rocky hill and stood looking across the open country. She was shaken with terror. Day after day and night after night terrible things had happened; the friendly young buck of her own herd had been killed by the leopard, she had become alone and friendless, she could not eat without dread of leopard or cheetah, nor drink without fear of the crocodile, and when she slept it was to awake amid the shouts and alarms of the baboons. And now this last terrible and incomprehensible enemy had come, filling her with a greater fear than any of the others. Even the warning of the baboons, in which she had trusted, had not availed against this moving, scorching thing which devoured even grass and trees.

The baboons above her head were still excitedly calling to each other, and without knowing why she felt that their protection would no longer be of any use to her. And she wanted to be far away from that hill, with its smoke-stained rocks and the devastated blackness of the ground beneath it.

She suddenly started running. Without caring where she went, she ran as it happened away from the river, straight across the plain towards the mountains which edged the valley several miles away. Forgetful of the fact that this was the hour when she would normally have gone to the river to drink, she ran on until at last fatigue compelled her to stop. She looked around her. The mountains were much nearer and surprisingly larger. She could distinguish trees growing on their sides and an odd white border at the top of them. Dusk was falling, but as she stood panting she knew that she would need to drink before night. Some distance ahead she could see a little dip in the ground, fringed with trees, and knowing that she might there find water she forced herself to go on again. She saw a small herd of oryx approaching the hollow from the opposite side, their heads, surmounted by straight, sharp horns, lowered as if they too had travelled far and were hardly able to keep their heads erect. The herd moved without their usual sentinels, eager only for water and disregarding danger from lions in their anxiety to reach the hollow. They came to its edge, slithered and leapt down a steep bank, staggered to the shallow water in its centre, and lowered their heads to drink.

The impalla joined them, drinking the water greedily. It was good to drink after a day of fear and heat and a long run. Before she had finished, the oryx, in spite of their anxiety to quench their thirst, suddenly stopped drinking and stood alert with heads raised. Then a large herd of zebra came to the pool, increasing their speed down the bank as they saw that they would not have the fast diminishing water to themselves. But when they reached the bottom of the hollow the females and youngsters drew back while the males pushed forward to be the first to drink. One young male, already a fine-looking creature, lingered for a second as if uncertain of his proper place, and then suddenly made up his mind and went forward; but two of the older males turned on him at once, pushing him with their noses to teach him not to be importunate.

When she had finished drinking, the impalla wandered to the opposite side of the pool, again feeling her loneliness and uncertain where to go. She walked among the waiting zebra and then stopped to nibble at a small clump of grass. The young zebra, fresh from his chastisement, lowered his head to graze beside her, and because she sniffed at him in a friendly manner and did not draw back, he returned to her after he had at last been allowed to go forward with the females to drink.

The impalla took that for a sign of the friendship of which she was badly in need; and when the zebra walked out of the hollow, she went with them, close beside the young male. She lay near him on the grass when the herd rested, and fed near him when they grazed. Like herself, the young zebra, though well-built, was still tiny, so that as they stood together in the centre of the herd the fully grown animals towered above them, giving them a feeling of safety; and indeed, whenever they grazed towards the outskirts of the herd the young zebra's mother followed and nosed him back.

In the early morning while the herd walked along, grazing, they passed an old kongoni, standing sentinel on an ant-hill whilst his companions were scattered about grazing. The impalla, because she already felt secure and happy among her new friends, began to play, leaping high into the air, turning quickly, leaping again. The young zebra, beside his mother, stood watching her. The mother was interested at these strange antics, and the youngster soon became eager to join in the game. He tried to leap as the impalla did; but while she leapt lightly and gracefully high into the air, and sprang again almost instantly, he could only make little short jumps, landing heavily on all four feet. He could not make out how she did it and tried again and again, always heavily and without anything to equal her quickness and lightness of foot.

Two days later, as the zebra and the impalla played together, the mother watching and the rest of the herd either grazing or slumbering in a dry watercourse, the sky darkened with a great cloud that descended over them. The oldest zebra looked up bewildered and then broke into a run, the whole herd following. The cloud fell slowly until it touched the ground and then broke into a hundred thousand small, moving pieces, each grey-green with strange markings and with wings —a swarm of locusts.

The impalla saw with amazement the colour of the ground change as these myriad insects descended on to it; she saw them alight on the back of the young zebra beside her and slip from it to the ground, except where they became entangled in his mane and tail. She felt them on her own head and body; she found herself treading on them at every step. There were so many that those she killed as she ran were instantly covered by others, still falling from the sky.

Under the weight of the locusts, blades of grass bent down. Now and then a single blade, suddenly released, would spring upright, and then a dozen insects would alight on it, bearing it down once more. The ground was hidden by a moving, bewildering mass. Birds came to feed on the locusts, flying from all parts to this grey-green patch on the borders of the plain, but the patch remained the same strange colour even after the birds had eaten several thousand insects.

The impalla ran with the herd of zebra, joining other herds all hurrying to escape. Over a mile of ground the locusts had settled, a swarm that in a day would destroy the vegetation almost as effectively as the fire had done on the ground nearer the river. Again and again the impalla

shook herself to get free of them, but those that
fell were immediately replaced by others. And
then, while the herds were still half a mile from
the edge of the swarm, a strong breeze suddenly
came, the living field rose from the ground like a
cloud, began to settle once more and then over all
that space it rose high into the air, swung and
billowed for a moment uncertainly in the wind,
and finally soared still higher to disappear into the
distance.

.   .   .   .   .

The locusts had gone. Yet even in that short
space of time the vegetation had been nibbled
short, so that trees were bare of leaves and
instead of the nine-inch blades of grass blowing
in the breeze, there was but a three-inch stubble,
littered with broken fragments of brownish-
green. The zebra lowered their heads to graze,
but that short grass no longer pleased them and
they made their way onwards beyond the track
of the swarm, past trees that looked like skeletons,
to the longer grass of the untouched plain.

There the several herds of zebra, oryx, eland
and gazelle that had run for a mile together, now
drifted apart, spreading out across the plain and
each finding its own spot on which to graze.

The impalla stayed with the zebra, keeping in the midst of the herd as it grazed slowly forward, one old male leading. Suddenly, on an open patch between two clumps of bushes, the male jumped to one side, as a cobra suddenly raised its head. Thirty yards away a white-breasted secretary bird, three feet high, walked to and fro, its eyes searching the grass for its food. The quick movement of the old zebra attracted its attention —it knew the cause immediately and ran with outspread wings to the spot. The cobra turned back to its hole, but before it could reach it the bird was dancing overhead, its sharp claws stamping on the cobra's body. Again and again the twisting snake struck with its poisonous fangs, but each time as it did so the bird leapt into the air, descending an instant later to renew its stamping. Finding itself unable to get rid of its attacker, the cobra at last lay still, hoping that the secretary bird would think it dead. But the bird had fought snakes before and was wily; it drew back a few feet and watched, and the moment the cobra, imagining itself alone, started to turn towards its hole, the bird pounced again, stamping with renewed energy. And when at last it knew the snake was dead it tore the body in two, carrying first one half and then the other to its nest.

The old zebra who had first seen the cobra had stopped for a minute to watch with a mild interest the fight between it and the secretary bird, the rest of the herd gathering in a group behind him. But such a scene was not uncommon in the jungle; in any case it was no concern of zebras and far less important than the business of slowly grazing forward in time to reach the river at dusk. So long before the fight was finished the old zebra led the way across the open.

Night was beginning to fall by the time they reached the bushes. There the leader drew a little further ahead, moving with careful suspicion, for he knew that this was the hour at which the lion might hunt. He went forward step by step, stopping suddenly and starting to turn back when, in the half light, bushes and trees seemed to come to life and move. The rest of the herd, and the young impalla among them, stopped when he stopped and advanced when he went on. They kept closely together as the well-worn path— worn by countless animals through hundreds of years—wound among the bushes. The impalla and the young male zebra were so small compared to the others that they could only see ahead when by chance a small gap appeared among the animals in front of them. They knew that there was danger, that they could not trust to their own senses and that their only protection was the fact that they were in the very centre of the herd. At any moment the leader might give the alarm, and then in the rout that would follow they might easily find themselves losing place and becoming left behind. Yet the impalla found some comfort in the fact that she and the young zebra were together, and she took care to keep very close beside him.

Suddenly she stopped, her heart beating wildly with terror, as from afar off there came the grunt of a lion. It came again and again, from higher up the river, now low and throaty, now like a deep, gruff sigh.

The terrifying sound reverberated among the trees, seeming to come now from one side, now from the other. For a second the herd stood wondering where to turn, then they all raced for open country. Cries of fear came from them as they galloped at a speed which would soon have left the impalla behind had she not been able to gain ground by leaping. She saw that the young zebra, with a speed that came from fear, was keeping almost level with her, and already she could see the light of the open plain through the tops of the bushes ahead. And then there came a terrible coughing roar just behind her right shoulder, she swerved violently to the left, and she knew, though she did not see, that a lioness had leapt from cover on to the back of a zebra. She heard, above the sound of flying hoofs, the agonised cry of that zebra, dying quickly, and then, her young friend still beside her, she was once more on the plain, galloping across it to safety.

" A fine looking creature."

" The young impalla kept close beside the zebra."

" The impalla stayed with the zebra."

CHAPTER
FOURTEEN

THE HYENA GOES HOME

WHILE the lion and the lioness lay beside the dead zebra, hyenas and jackals, like dark grey shadows among the bushes, gathered from all sides to wait for the remains of the feast. They were impatient, yet they did not dare to venture close. With increasing frequency as the minutes passed, the hyenas wailed or "laughed" in the excitement of hunger; gleaming eyes from the darkness showed them standing alert; a sound of soft movement betrayed them as they circled stealthily round and round. But till the lions had finished they would keep their distance; only once did a hyena—bold because he was young and inexperienced—venture forward, and instantly the lion with an angry growl sent him scuttling back into the shadows.

But at last the lion rose, yawning and stretching himself, and turned towards the river. The

lioness too was well satisfied, yet she had difficulty in leaving the feast. She lay tearing off bits
of meat and then, as if her lord had called, she
too rose to her feet, took one last look at the kill,
and moved slowly away.

Then it was the turn of the hyenas, who rushed
in, hurriedly eating their fill and tearing off larger
pieces which they would carry to their lair as a
meal for their families. Only when they rose
could the jackals take their turn, to eat what they
could until daybreak when they would be driven
away by the kites, marabou storks and vultures.

Four of the hyenas, each laden with a lump of
meat, started away from the kill in single file,
spread out twenty or thirty yards apart. They
were great, awkward-looking creatures, big-
headed, fierce-jawed, their backs sloping downward from shoulder to rump. Very silently they
moved towards the river, passing close under
bushes along a track that led to their lair, a
quarter of a mile further down the stream.

Suddenly, some fifty yards from the river-
bank, the leader stopped, standing alert with ears
forward, listening. Out from the bushes ahead
two more of their own pack approached—females
coming from the lair to see what spoil their mates

had brought. For a minute the two leaders stood a yard apart as if suspiciously watching each other, while those behind closed up. Then the party from the kill, well laden, went on, the others turning to accompany them. But one of the four suddenly dropped his burden at his mate's feet and turned back. It was for him to scavenge at the kill, for her to fetch and carry. With a silent, furtive gait, he went back by the way he had come.

He went straight back to the kill. The first warnings of daylight were already lightening the sky, and high overhead a solitary vulture, having sighted the feast, was planing down, while others, far above him, were circling, each time lower, till presently they too would alight. The jackals, busy at their meal, were becoming nervous in the increasing light, with the knowledge that it was all but time for them to be away.

The hyena gave a short, grunting squeal as he rushed in to seize another portion of meat. He wrenched off part of a leg, almost too awkward for him to carry, setting his teeth at the middle joint so that half stuck out on either side of his jaws, then turned swiftly and went back among the bushes, his head pulled this way and that as the ends of the bone were caught by branches.

Beneath a tree not far from the river he stopped, setting down the bone to get a more secure grip of it. Then suddenly he raised his head, nose turned to the left, body alert, nostrils quivering, as he heard the scratch-scratch of a mongoose tearing at the remains of something behind a neighbouring bush. Guessing that there lay a further meal (left, perhaps, by a serval cat) he stood hesitating, thinking of the heavy bone that had been so awkward to carry, yet unwilling to lose this chance of yet more food. But even if he would be unable to carry it away, he could not resist the temptation to see what was there. So leaving the bone beneath the tree, he turned aside.

At the sound of his coming the mongoose scuttled off, leaving his treasure behind him. It was only the remains of a guinea-fowl, poor food compared to zebra-meat, and there was precious little of it except a tangled mass of feathers. But the hyena took it in his teeth, one tattered wing trailing down to the ground, and started back to see if he could not somehow contrive to carry it at the same time as the zebra leg.

By the entrance to the little clearing that sur-rounded the tree he stopped, alert and on guard once more. Along a low branch lay a python, eighteen feet or more in length, its head hanging down towards the ground; and as the hyena watched, it slid forward till its head and the front half of its body were on the earth, while its tail was still entwined among the branches of the tree.

Though the python was not interested in the meat which the hyena had left on the ground, it happened that its descent from the tree took it so close that the hyena, watching with a greedy suspicion, assumed that he would lose his prize. He was by nature a coward—but he would fight for his own belongings, particularly that morning when he knew that he had secured more food than any other member of the pack. So he dropped the guinea-fowl and leaped forward. The python drew back along the ground with its head raised, its body in a gigantic S-shaped curve; but the hyena turned swiftly to follow, and charged in, his teeth closing with a snap within an inch of the python's body. The python, at the same moment, struck suddenly downward, its head crossing the hyena's back: its coils closed on his body, and as the hyena bit again the encircling coils drew closer and tighter, throwing him to the ground and half throttling him; but the

117

hyena's second bite had been successful, his teeth had fastened themselves into the snake's body, and with a snarl of anger he worried and tore at the flesh.

Though he was almost strangled, the hyena would not loosen his hold, and he held on until at last he tore away a portion of the python's body, close behind its head. Then, suddenly, the coils relaxed, the tail fell limply from the tree, and the python lay quivering in death.

Drawing himself out of that enfolding mass the hyena shook himself, looked down at the dead body of the snake, smelt it, shook himself again, and then picked up his spoils, the zebra leg and the mangled remains of the half-eaten guinea-fowl. Before he had moved a couple of yards the bird fell from his grasp, but he bit again, catching the tip of its wing, and carried it dragging between his legs.

He went to his home, a series of narrow tunnels in a clump of rocks close to the river, which was shared by three families. It was like a warren, dark and evil smelling. A few bones lay outside the entrance and with one of them two young hyenas were playing. Inside the tunnels the five hyenas crouched on the floor eating what

118

they had brought that night, crushing the bones in their jaws.

The meal was almost ended by the time the hyena laid his zebra bone and the guinea-fowl on the floor beside his mate; but she turned to share that food with him, wrenching meat from the bone while her two youngsters crept up to eat what was left of the fowl. Only when all but a few scattered fragments of flesh had been eaten did the hyenas settle themselves to sleep through the day, lying close together, a mass of unkempt dark grey hair, on the floor of the noisome tunnel.

CHAPTER
FIFTEEN

THE MOTHER GIRAFFE

DURING the weeks that followed the young
impalla continued to live among the zebra,
not so much because she acquired any special
feeling of safety amongst them as because she had
found companionship. The young zebra was
always with her, playing or grazing or sleeping.
He took her part in the not infrequent quarrels
which came when the animals pushed past one
another in their haste to reach the water or to
choose the best patches of shade, and she found
that by keeping close to him she could often
secure a better place than she would ever have
been allowed to get by herself.

The herd as a whole regarded her with but
little interest. Now and then an inquisitive and
quarrelsome old male would come up to her,
butting her with his nose as if to remind her that
she was an alien and unwanted among zebras,

but for the most part she was not interfered with and was allowed to take her place with other junior members of the herd. And as the days passed the mother of the young zebra came to regard the impalla almost as one of her own family. When the young zebra strayed, his mother would nose him into a position of greater safety and then she would return and do the same thing to the impalla, urging her towards the centre of the herd and nosing at her flanks if she did not move fast enough. And when the roar of a lion was heard or the crocodiles took toll or some other danger threatened, the mother, after seeing that her own offspring was close to her side, would look around to make sure that the impalla was in safety also.

For the herd was by now very nervous. In a week after the lion's kill one of their number had fallen victim to the crocodiles, and although perforce they still went regularly to the river to drink, they would hesitate and go back and come again perhaps half a dozen times before they felt convinced that they could safely venture to the water's edge. At all times of the day and night they were more suspicious than usual, jumping at shadows or even at the sudden movement of birds, showing less faith in their own sentinels and continually raising their heads to stare and listen while they grazed.

Moreover, their fear soon spread to other herds. When other zebra or gazelle or wildebeest saw their watchfulness or noted how they jumped at the slightest sudden sound, they too, in their turn, showed an extra caution, which bred nervousness and dread even amongst those who did not know what was the danger. The news spread. Sometimes a herd, fresh from another part of the plain, would realise at once that greater caution than was normal was here being used; they would see the jumpiness of their fellows and immediately become nervous themselves. Elephant and rhinoceros took the infection of fear, as did the little mongoose and the rock-rabbit. Even the lions themselves, part-originators of this terror, saw the uneasiness of the animals they stalked, realised that it was greater than usual, and without knowing the cause of it, became in some degree infected with it, so that they too showed an additional wariness and caution.

And while this happened, the young lion cubs grew up and as they grew they required more food. The necessity for hunting thus became more frequent, although the extra nervousness of the animals made success less sure. More than once the lion and the lioness went out in the night but failed to kill; and then the cubs were hungry and peevish the next day. So cautious were the herds that they would move off at top speed at the slightest suspicion, where previously they would have waited, alert but motionless, until suspicion ripened—and in that time the lion's stalk would often have been successful. Once the lioness stalked the herd of zebra in which the impalla lived, for more than two hours, following them through bush and grass which provided her with sufficient concealment. At the end she sprang, aiming as usual for the neck and shoulders; but the first slight rustle of the grass caused the zebra to jump, so that she landed only half across its hind-quarters, her claws tearing its skin in long scratches as the zebra, lashing out with hind feet, kicked her stomach and broke away.

Early one morning, after a fruitless night, the lioness returned to the lair and her cubs while the lion continued to hunt. Through long brown grass which barely covered his back, he crept, moving stealthily so that no pronounced motion of the blades of grass should betray his presence. He sighted a herd of wildebeest returning from the river and crept after them. At a distance of a hundred and fifty yards he crouched, knowing that if he approached closer while the sentinels of the herd were facing towards him he would be seen at once and the wildebeest would scamper away. But if, without any movement on his part, the animals should come closer, feeding as they came, he might then be able to draw nearer still under cover of the grass—near enough to be able to charge.

But although at first the herd came slowly but steadily forward, the sentinels soon became uneasy, standing still and peering towards the hidden lion. As they stopped, the herd behind them also stopped, as yet unalarmed and continuing to graze, but ready to bolt the instant the alarm was given. At last one of the two sentinels ventured a few yards further. Then, though the lion made no movement, the wildebeest was suddenly overcome by his suspicions and without further enquiry he turned and bolted. Instantly the other sentinel and the whole herd thundered away across the stretch of open land.

124

Without raising his back above the top of the sea of grass the lion turned and moved away. It was useless for him to pursue the stampeded herd; other prey could just as easily be found, and then perhaps his stalk would be more fortunate.

Under a group of trees some little distance away, a herd of giraffe were standing, their heads among the leaves, their patterned bodies and necks almost indistinguishable until they moved. Yet the lion saw them and since nothing else was in sight he began to stalk them.

Nearer and nearer he came without arousing suspicion. He saw that there were five fully grown giraffe and one very small youngster. He knew that though the herd could gallop away, easily outdistancing him, the young one would be quickly caught if the others deserted it; and he crept forward so as to cut it off from the rest of the herd. Its mother stood close beside it, her front legs spread wide as she slowly lowered her head and began to rub her nose against a low ant-hill. Then, startled as the lion drew near, she suddenly looked up, gazing into the lion's eyes as they showed through the thinning blades of grass.

Though she could make no noise, the rest of
the herd, now separated from her by the clump
of trees, knew instantly that there was cause for
alarm and with their tails twirling aloft in the air
they raced away. For a second the mother giraffe
seemed to think of following them; then she
turned to her youngster and shepherding it before
her she set off as quickly as its shorter legs could
move. As she followed in the direction taken by
the herd, already disappearing into the distant
haze, she repeatedly cast anxious glances behind
her; and the lion, no longer troubling to stalk
her, drew quickly nearer, openly and with none
of his usual wariness.

The mother giraffe quickly realised that escape
was impossible. Turning to face the lion, she
nosed her youngster into the only place of
comparative safety—the space beneath her body,
between her fore and hind legs.

Balanced there on her thin, spindle-like legs,
she must have appeared no match for the lion;
yet for the moment she and her young one were
safe. The lion, instead of advancing, began
slowly to circle round her, never encroaching on
the thirty yards of ground that separated them,
keeping his eyes steadily on his prey and ready

to escape the giraffe's only weapon which he regarded as too deadly to allow of nearer approach.
For if he came within range, the giraffe's front
foot would suddenly shoot out with enormous
force—a kick that might easily disable him; or
if without coming so close he nevertheless drew
a little nearer and for an instant shifted his gaze,
she might run forward, steady herself for a
second and then launch that terrible kick so
strongly as to break his shoulder.

As the lion circled, seeking the moment when
he could rush in without danger to himself, the
giraffe turned, so that her face was always towards
the lion and her front legs were continually ready
for action. And all the time, while she turned
and manœuvred, she kept her youngster in its
refuge under her body.

Many times the lion circled round her. Once
the baby giraffe became confused among its
mother's movements and stepped for an instant
out of its shelter. Thinking that his chance of
securing that tender meal had come, the lion
ventured closer; instantly the mother giraffe
stepped quickly forward and struck a deadly
blow which missed him by inches—then she
recovered herself and before the lion could take

advantage of her lack of poise she was again astride her youngster and at bay.

To the baby giraffe that was an hour of terror. It saw the lion continually circling, shutting off escape, it heard his terrible coughs, it became worried and confused amid its fright by the constant turning and by the gentle blows which it received from its mother's hind legs whenever it failed to turn as she turned. Its head just touched its mother's body, and from between her front legs it stared in utter terror at the lion.

An hour passed. For all that time the mother stood at bay, turning slowly, never too much and never too little, her eyes never leaving the lion's head, seeing every plan for sudden movement, every threatened spring. But as the heat of the sun grew more blazing, the tenseness of the lion's attitude began to relax. Once he stopped and stood watching the giraffe as if uncertain whether to risk a sudden attack. Then he recommenced his slow circling, but his eyes followed the movements of the giraffe less surely and again and again he seemed to hesitate, on the point of turning away. Then suddenly he turned and went, without once looking behind him, towards his lair.

" With their tails twirling aloft in the air they raced away."

" The mother giraffe."

The mother giraffe watched till he was out of sight, then she put down her long neck to nose the youngster in the right direction, and began quietly to shepherd it in the path taken by the rest of the herd.

THE WILD DOGS

ALTHOUGH the impalla was happy among the zebra she had not forgotten her own herd nor ceased to wish that she could find them. From time to time during those weeks, impalla would come near and with a sudden flutter of excitement she would go to see if they were those she knew. But they were always strangers to her, and although more than once she was tempted to join them for the sake of being again with her own kind, her friendship with the young zebra and the feeling that she was at home amongst his herd made her hesitate. And she soon discovered that she could not be sure of a welcome from these other herds of impalla; they were often far more suspicious of her and far less friendly than the zebra had been.

So she stayed where she was, gradually becoming contented with her lot. She learned to

" Lapping eagerly, but always watchful."

" The blurred grey outline of a herd of elephants."

→

↑ " The impalla moved to one side of the herd."

adopt the zebra's methods of caution, to pick up instantly their signals of danger, even to feel, not as an individual, but as a member of the herd. The fears she had had when she wandered alone, the anticipations of terror, lessened and finally vanished; but when the herd became particularly shy, she shared their nervousness, when they suddenly bolted, though perhaps none knew what was the danger, she experienced the palpitating terror of the stampeding herd.

One evening, as the zebra grazed towards the river, she suddenly came upon signs among the grass which reminded her of her own folk. Undoubtedly impalla had passed that way but a short time before; and though she could not be certain, she was filled with the suspicion that here at last was the herd into which she had been born and from which she had parted only a few weeks before.

For a minute she was torn between two instincts: a feeling that she must keep in the midst of the zebra, deriving safety from their sentinels, —and a desire to wander away, following the trail upon the grass, alone and unprotected once again, but always drawing nearer to her own friends.

As she hesitated, the zebra drew away till they came to the beginning of the path that led to the river. Already the impalla was separated from them, she was apart from the herd, and with the realisation of that, the desire to roam by herself increased. So she turned away to follow the trail.

It led her across an open patch of country, with her back to the river. She forgot her desire to drink, forgot everything except the growing conviction that her friends had indeed passed that way and that in a few minutes she would be amongst them.

.   .   .   .   .

Under a group of trees a hundred yards away lay a pack of wild dogs. There were twelve of them, strong and fierce, with legs made for speed and strength made for killing. Like the leopard and the lion they were a constant cause of terror to the herds. Their victims were antelope or gazelle who ventured to wander alone or who, being outmanœuvred, could be cut off so that they ran through panic in the wrong direction. Then the dogs would race in pursuit, spreading out in a half-circle to surround their victim; and so swift were they that their success was almost

132

inevitable. They would kill, eating savagely and leaving little for the scavengers. Then, with the thirst that came from the drinking of blood, they would trot to the river to drink, lapping eagerly, but watchful always for the crocodile—the one enemy whose speed over a short distance they could barely equal and whose fearsome snout might rise from the water without warning and as quickly drag them to death.

Now, ten of the pack lay dozing, heads on paws, while two stood alert, nostrils quivering as the breeze reached them, watching for their prey. Suddenly one of the two gave a quick, short yelp. Instantly the pack was on its feet following him. After a dozen yards another dog gave tongue and sprang to the front. Then, sure at last of their prey, the whole pack dashed forward.

As if by instinct the impalla looked up at that moment from the ground. Seeing the pack she turned to run, leaving the trail she had followed, in her anxiety to race in the opposite direction from the dogs. She was compelled to run up-wind, leaving strong scent behind her, and the long jumps which she took showed her clearly to her pursuers; but she had no thought of that nor of anything save of running with all the strength and speed of her limbs, straight from the advancing pack.

Terror possessed her. She knew that the dogs were overtaking her, in deadly pursuit. She had no refuge, nowhere to hide, no chance of safety except in her own speed—and that was failing her. Behind her the pack spread out, two of the dogs on either side racing as if to head her off if she turned either to the river or towards the mountains. They too gained rapidly upon her, so that it seemed that very soon she would be surrounded.

Yet she could not think of that, nor of anything save to run and run, with terror-stricken speed. She was far too terrified to turn or to choose any special direction except straight ahead. Fatigue came but she hardly noticed it. Fright caught her breath so that her heart palpitated and she panted as she ran; but she dared not slacken speed and could only run on and on, blindly, hopelessly, without thought, with almost paralysing terror of the danger that was swiftly drawing close behind her.

And then, as she panted over the crest of a slight incline, her starting eyes saw immediately

134

below her the blurred grey outline of a herd of elephants.

They stood in a group directly in front of her, and she was too much spent to turn aside to pass them, just as she was too much blinded by fear to realise that in them was her one chance of safety. From three sides the dogs were closing in on her, lips drawn back and teeth bared. But they too saw the elephants and those on either flank swung outwards to pass them. The impalla leapt on-wards. For one brief instant she saw a grey towering mass above her with an opening like a gateway beneath it, and into that gateway, be-tween the legs of the nearest elephant and under its body, she ran. The dogs, now very close to her heels, checked suddenly as their quarry vanished into the midst of the herd. On the further side of the elephants the dogs that had run on either flank stood panting, and suddenly one of them howled in rage and disappointment. Then as if with one accord they drew away, the pack reunited and lay down beneath a near-by tree, watching with eager eyes the herd of ele-phants whose presence had robbed them of the prey they had so nearly secured.

CHAPTER
SEVENTEEN

ELEPHANTS

WHEN she found herself completely surrounded by those massive grey forms the
impalla suddenly felt very much the same feeling
of protection which she had experienced when
she stood in the middle of the herd of zebra. But
the danger was now more acute, the protecting
animals were far bigger. Moreover, her straight,
headlong course was impossible through the
midst of the herd; she would have to walk
slowly and windingly round the huge bodies of
the elephants, now darting under the body of an
old bull, now turning aside to pass a calf. And
as, with the terror of the pursuit still upon her,
she began to make her difficult way forward,
the instinct of safety which comes from the
presence of a surrounding herd made her look
back.

For a moment she could see nothing but the

elephants; then, as a cow elephant raised her
trunk, a small gap appeared in the grey and
through it the impalla saw the wild dogs going
away. She stopped then, and even went back a
little, but keeping still within the ramparts of the
herd, till she could see the dogs more clearly.
She saw them reach a tree and lie down beneath
it; she knew that they had not forgotten her nor
entirely abandoned the chase—that they were
waiting and watching for her to leave her protection so that they might catch her. But she had
no intention of doing that. The feeling she had
recently acquired of safety in numbers and the
fear of loneliness returned to her, and she went
back to the centre of the herd, keeping pace with
the elephants as they travelled slowly forward.

Close to her walked a cow elephant with her
calf. The calf was but a few days old, so that
now and then it would give a little shambling
trot to keep up with its mother, and then, as if it
had felt the fear of being left behind, it would
put its little trunk across its mother's trunk to
assure itself that all was well and that to walk by
its mother's side was the safest thing in the
world.

A bull elephant, well on in years with skin

137

wrinkled and creased, led the herd down what appeared to be a well-trampled path. They went slowly, pulling clumps of grass with their trunks and pushing them into their mouths. And the impalla, seeing that and realising that the wild dogs were still beneath a tree that was now fading into the distance, forgot her fears and began to graze.

As the herd advanced, away from the river to which they had been for water, they reached fresh country where the grass grew so high that it reached almost to the level of the back of the tallest elephant; but on this path, well worn by the daily passage of the herd, the grass was pressed flat. The impalla, traversing that broad avenue, saw the high grass on either side, heard it swish against the flanks of the elephants that walked on the outside of the herd, and felt a sudden tremor of fear. But it did not long bother her, for she felt completely at ease among her strange companions. Instinct told her that these animals were not afraid. They had no sentinels as the baboons, the zebra and her own kind would have had; the old bull a few paces in advance of the rest, was more a leader than a scout, and other big bulls brought up the rear. And the absence of nervousness was so apparent

amongst the herd that several of the youngsters
stopped to play, entwining their trunks and
wrestling, falling out of place in the engrossment
of the game, and then hurrying to catch up.
Nobody seemed to mind if these youngsters
lingered; the only anxiety was when a very small
calf became separated from its mother, perhaps
by some bigger elephant pressing between them,
and then the mother would stand swishing her
trunk from side to side until she discovered where
the calf had gone.

Presently the herd left the high grass and came
to a clump of strong trees in a clearing, where the
leader stopped. The trunks of these trees were
worn to a polished smoothness where generations
of elephants, the parents and grandparents of the
herd, had rubbed and scraped their sides against
them. Now bull elephants and cow elephants
went to the trees, laboriously rubbing, heaving
their sides up and down, and turning so that both
flanks might benefit; and the calves, tuskless and
of tenderer skin, imitated their parents whenever
they could find an unoccupied place closer to the
roots.

Then once more the herd started forward,
into the heart of a thick forest, still by the trodden

path, till they reached an open space which they themselves had cleared of trees in days gone by. There, for a minute, the leader stood, his trunk in the air and his ears spread out, listening and trying to pick up the sound or scent of anything that might disturb the night; then, seemingly satisfied, he settled himself to sleep, still standing but swaying rhythmically from side to side in time with his breathing. The mother elephants made sure that their calves were close at hand, then the entire herd prepared for sleep, all upright, all gently swaying.

As she felt the sudden silence and stillness around her the young impalla found for an instant that the past feeling of insecurity returned to her. Under the broad body of the nearest elephant she stared into the darkness of the forest, where trees and bushes seemed, as she looked, to take strange shapes, even to move. She remained alert, half uncertain whether she should stay where she was or run away. But she could not run alone into that darkness, making her way among shadows from which danger might suddenly spring, under trees from which leopard or cheetah might pounce, running she knew not where and risking she knew not what.

Better, far, to stay in this half-security, among these creatures who showed no wish to harm her and who, only a short time before, had seemed to her the most perfect protection.

Choosing a spot in the centre of the herd of swaying giants she lay down. Then, the great bodies of the elephants loomed like mountains far above her, their legs surrounded her like a forest, and a sense of peace and security returned.

. . . . .

At daybreak she awoke, to find the elephants already stirring. The cow elephant beside whom she had slept moved towards the edge of the clearing, and the impalla jumped up hastily to avoid being crushed. She moved a little distance, lowering her head to graze. A calf came close to her, his trunk raised, inspecting her and seeming to ask who she was and why she was there. But though curious he was not really surprised at her presence, for he had often seen zebra, gazelle and impalla grazing quite close to his herd.

Presently the herd started on a long trek, back along the beaten path, eating as they went. They passed through the forest, across the stretch of high elephant grass, over the open country, past the single tree under which the disappointed dogs had rested the night before and from which they had long since vanished, through the tract of thorn trees, bushes and undergrowth, and so to the bank of the river. They moved very silently, crossing the sandbank and stepping at last into the shallows at its edge, where they stood squirting water over themselves or else lay down, rolling and splashing with complete enjoyment.

The impalla, feeling by that time very thirsty, moved to the other side of the sandbank and lowered her head towards the water. But before she dared to drink she looked anxiously across the pool, seeking the one thing she feared there —the monster that moved so silently in it. She hesitated at the sight of ripples on the surface, half turning to run; but then she realised that they spread outwards as the water was stirred by the elephants. She saw hippos bobbing up and down at the further end of the pool, but they did not alarm her. She saw, almost without noticing it, something like a long, flat log of wood lying on an island, but it was motionless and inanimate and she did not give it a second thought. All seemed still in the river and gratefully she began to drink.

Suddenly some instinct caused her to raise her

142

" Something moved, like the end of a log."

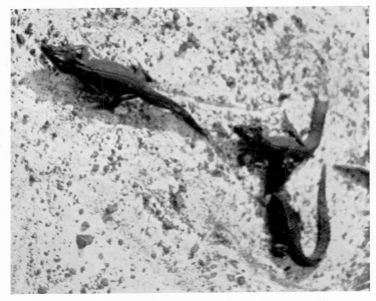

" The baby crocodiles were less than four inches long."

head. In the water not far away something moved, like the end of a log. And as she realised that, she saw also that the log which a moment before had lain on the island was no longer there.

She did not wait. Though there was very little in that moving object which she could recognise, she knew what it was; she knew that the terror of the river, in dread of which she had lived in weeks past, was again upon her. In an instant the crocodile would rise above the surface, with two small eyes fastening themselves upon her, seeming to hold her immovable. . . . With fear once again clutching her heart, she turned and ran.

But she was hardly across the sandbank and into the protecting bushes when she stopped. She did not believe that the crocodile could harm her there. They did not spring from the ground, in hiding amongst bushes, as the lion did, nor from trees like the leopard. The danger from them was only at the waterside. She had seen several animals caught at the sandbank; even while stampeding from danger she had had swift visions of them caught by leg or neck and dragged under the water. But not among these bushes, which, although they might have hidden lion or cheetah, now suddenly seemed a protection.

It was that that she needed. If she were now to run past these bushes and trees and into the open country she would once more be at the mercy of wild dogs or would be stalked by some even fiercer creature. Only when in the midst of a herd, whether of her own kind or of zebra, baboons or elephants, had she felt anything approaching safety.

So she turned again, keeping close to the protecting bushes and along the edge of the sandbank till she was once more amongst the elephants. She would rather have rejoined the herd of zebra, because of the youngster with whom she had made friends, but she had no idea where they had gone. And the elephants, at the least, would not harm her.

They were out of the water now, covering themselves with showers of dust, blown through their trunks. Particles of that dust fell on her back as she approached, giving her an uncomfortable feeling of dirtiness; but the elephants enjoyed it, liking the feel of it on their backs. Presently they began slowly moving away, rejoining the path by which they had arrived and causing a herd of kongoni and a few gazelle to stand aside out of their way.

The impalla, in the midst of them, began suddenly to fear the crossing of the open country. Even in the safety of their hugeness she found that she no longer wanted to cross the open again nor to traverse that avenue through the high-growing grass. More than ever before she wanted to be with her own herd, or at least with some herd of gazelle with whom she had kinship. Even at the price of renewed danger she wanted to be able to run and to leap, to have animals grazing around her when she grazed, to rely upon the sentinels of a herd, to be able to lie down to sleep with the knowledge that she was among friends. These mighty elephants, though far from hostile, were indifferent to her. Even the baboons had troubled to warn her of danger; but the elephants would not do that, would not care, would only serve as an inanimate bulwark behind which she might hide. If she left them now, if for lack of the supreme joy of reaching her own herd, she joined the kongoni, or better still the gazelle, she would at least feel that she was closer to home.

So she turned aside, making her way through the narrow space between a cow elephant and its calf, stepping under the swinging trunk of an old

K   145

bull as he reached for leaves from a tree, and came to the rear of the gazelle.

Then as she stood amongst them she suddenly felt more completely at peace than she had done at any moment since leaving her own herd.

CHAPTER
EIGHTEEN

CROCODILE EGGS

A S the dry season advanced the volume of water in the river became appreciably less, more and more of the banks became exposed, and the water of the pool also drew away so that it spread over less of the sandbank; and whereas at one time the animals had been able to drink a few yards from the bushes, they now had to cross nearly twice that distance, with greater uncertainty as to what might lurk behind them.

Yet although that gave the giant crocodile a greater chance of catching his prey before it could race to safety, he had also greater difficulty in concealing himself in the channel behind the sandbank, for there too the water had become shallow. Often he would start to swim into that channel, only to find himself aground on the shelving sand long before he had reached the true strategical position for his attack; then he would retire, try to get closer on the opposite side of the channel, or else swim round to try his luck from the front of the sandbank.

At the same time he found the animals showing a new wariness as they came to drink. He did not know the reason of it, nor did the reason trouble him. He was only concerned with making his capture and when an animal started and fled before he was near enough to strike, he merely settled himself to wait for another or swam to a different part of the sandbank to see if his chances would there be greater.

Meanwhile the young crocodile whom he had chosen months before as his mate had now laid twelve eggs, each a little bigger than a hen's egg, and had buried them in the sand that bordered one side of their little creek. She did not have to concern herself with hatching them; the heat of the sun would do that, and meantime she could hunt beside the giant crocodile, swim with him in the pool, or lie lazily in the shallow water of the creek or beside the eggs on the shelf of mud and sand.

But one day, while the giant crocodile and his mate were watching at the sandbank, a monitor, broad of back with a long, thin neck and head, crept inch by inch down the sloping stem of a tree towards the sand in which the eggs were buried. It moved with its body pressed flat against the wood, pulling itself along very slowly by means of its claws. Behind it, its long tail, not unlike that of the crocodiles, stretched out, swinging occasionally from side to side. It came on, with slow relentlessness, till it reached the sand, and then with its front claws it began to dig. An egg was soon unearthed, picked up in the monitor's mouth and carried to its home. Minutes passed, then back came the monitor to dig a second egg from the sand and carry it away with the same care lest its teeth should crush the shell before all was ready for the feast.

In this way four eggs were taken. The monitor was descending from the tree for a fifth when it suddenly raised its head, emitted a long hiss, turned, and crawled back as the giant crocodile, followed by his mate, forced his way through the hanging gate of undergrowth that guarded the entrance to the creek.

The monitor, though it showed its anger at the disturbance in that hiss, did not hurry unduly; nor was there need for it to do so. The crocodiles drew themselves out of the water and on to the shelf, saw the scratched-up sand where the eggs had been buried, and then without any signs of distress turned in the water of the creek and settled down peacefully to bask in the heat of the sun.

Once again, a week later, the monitor raided the creek, devouring five more of the eggs before being disturbed; but after that it was busy elsewhere, laying its own eggs and burying them in the sand exactly after the manner of the crocodile. And so the three remaining eggs out of the dozen which the crocodile had laid were at last hatched out, and three creatures, incredibly tiny but the exact image of their parents, made their appearance.

For a week after their arrival on earth the baby crocodiles were less than six inches long; but they grew rapidly, crawling about the edge of the water and swimming in the creek, catching infinitesimal fish and occasionally playing or fighting on the shelf of mud. Their parents paid little or no attention to them, leaving them to find their own food and, as they grew bigger, to do their own exploring of the creek and its neighbourhood. Not until many months later, when the youngsters had grown even yet more like greatly reduced replicas of the giant, would they go out into the pool in search of larger fish.

The giant crocodile, had he ever been able to look ahead to those days, would have thought first of the return of the rain, the filling up of the river and pool and the consequent dearth of animals at the sandbank when water-holes on the patches of open country were easier and safer for drinking. After that, a dry season would follow, the animals would return to the river and life would once more be good for crocodiles.

. . . . .

Yet as it happened, for the giant crocodile those days were never to come.

CHAPTER
NINETEEN

THE RIVAL BABOONS

FOR some weeks past the life of the baboons on their hill had become increasingly precarious. Day after day and night after night the troop suffered loss from the attacks of leopards, who found their hunting easier because the old baboon who led the troop had grown slow and careless in giving the alarm.

He had led them for several years, settling their differences and quarrels as well as watching for danger. At first he had been very agile in climbing trees to look on all sides for glints of yellow fur among the bushes, and very quick in clambering from his post at the top of the hill to interfere when youngsters began to fight. But lately he had become less active. Often he would sit half asleep, with his hands drooping between his knees, and only the loudest of quarrels would make him rouse himself; and sometimes when he

152

was on guard his old eyes would become dim so that he would be a second late—a fatal second—in seeing danger, and the cry of a half-grown baboon as it felt the leopard's claws would set the troop in panic before he gave his warning shout.

One night a leopard raided the hill and departed with a young baboon in its teeth; a few hours later it returned for a second victim and again succeeded in killing without any warning being given. Then the anger of the troop was turned as much against their own leader as against the killer. For all the rest of that night the baboons shouted, while the leader sat apart, on a spur of rock, the one silent being on the hill. He knew how their anger had turned against himself, but he was still their leader, like a king on his throne facing a revolutionary mob. He had no thought of abdication or of flight; and later, when most of the baboons were quieter, he would clamber down and chastise some of the youngsters, to teach them that he still had authority, that he was powerful and strong and that their part was to obey his orders.

But suddenly, in the early morning, another male, almost fully grown and of great strength, climbed to the top of the hill and stood within a few feet of the old leader, his lips drawn back and his teeth bared.

The leader knew the meaning of that approach and that it was a challenge to his leadership. He moved forward on all fours, swinging slightly from side to side, his teeth ready to bite. He had no hesitation. He knew that he kept his position only because of his strength and that any baboon who challenged, fought and defeated him would take his place.

He leapt at his enemy, who raised himself to meet the onslaught. In a second the two baboons were mixed in a confused struggle, each seeking to hold and to bite.

They fought fiercely, striking and snapping, and all the while barking and shouting. When they bit, they let go immediately, seeking to bite again elsewhere. They fought on the spur of rock where the leader had sat, back across the summit of the hill, down again on to the spur and over its edge, then down to a lower rock. They disregarded falls, ignored the blood that ran from their wounds.

But though the challenging baboon was strong, the old leader had still the exceptional strength and skill with which, years before, he had won his position in the troop. His eyes might occasionally grow dim, he might be less agile in climbing and less active in interference, but when he was roused to great anger he could still fight with an unequalled ferocity. Gradually his strength and weight gave him the upper hand. He forced his enemy against a cliff of rock, held him there for a second, and then suddenly tried to bite savagely at his neck.

The baboon struggled hard, but he could not hold those long teeth away, could not prevent them coming nearer and nearer until in another instant they would have closed on a vital spot. And then, with a sudden twist, he slipped aside and ran away.

It meant defeat. He had failed to sustain his challenge, he had saved his life only by breaking off the fight. He would never be accepted by the troop as their leader, even when the old male died. And he would be despised as a weakling who had fought and been defeated.

Without looking back he climbed further down the rock. Baboons that he passed made way for him, stepping out of his path; youngsters ran out of his way and clambered to their mothers' breasts. Presently his mate followed him, with one baby clinging to her body and an older youngster walking by her side.

They went into exile, silently driven from the troop, and the old leader, stiff, sore and bleeding, resumed his position on the spur by the summit of the hill, in undisputed sway. No baboon then dared to show anger against him and the hill was quiet.

.   .   .   .   .

The baboons that had been driven out made their way towards the river, where the male stopped to look cautiously across the water and then drank and washed his wounds. Then they went to a rock close to the river-bank and climbed to the top of it.

That rock became their home. It contained a single small cave in which they lived; for the rest, they sat on the summit, looking down on to the river or into the bushes and the paths by which the animals came to drink. Daily they visited the glades in search of food, a troop of four, and when they met the bigger troop they climbed into the trees or hurried off at top speed.

At night they were watchful, knowing that enemies would soon discover their presence on the small rock and know that it was easier of access than the larger hill. They watched for that tell-tale streak of yellow broken with black which showed the approach of the leopard. At the slightest suspicion they shouted, and then the youngsters clung frantically and in terror to their parents.

Although the baboons left the rock daily in search of food, they often remained at their vantage point from which they could see the dark shape of the crocodiles in the river long before the animals on the bank could be suspicious of moving ripples. Then they would shout, and the news of danger would come, not only to their own youngsters, but also to the animals on the ground below. Again and again, as the giant crocodile approached the shore, the warning was given and zebra, gazelle and water-buck looked up and bolted away.

With this new protection, the animals were able to drink in greater safety. As the days passed the herds grew accustomed to relying as much on the shouts of the baboons on the rock as on their own sight, hearing and instinct. The shallow channel by the side of the sandbank could be seen from the top of the rock, and directly a grey snout appeared on the surface, with long body and tail more indistinctly following below the water, the baboons shouted and the animals raced to safety. No animal ever questioned the accuracy of that warning, nor stayed to see whether there was still time to drink; at the sound all turned and bolted into the shelter of the bushes, only venturing back half an hour later, and then hesitating, with ears cocked, lest another warning should be given.

At first the crocodiles did not realise the new difficulty which had come into their lives. They too heard the shout as they swam into the channel and they knew that for a time they were robbed of the chance of securing their prey. But they went on to the narrowest part of the channel, where they could lie, with their front legs resting on land beneath the surface and their tails afloat, and there they waited. Their small eyes would see the first hesitant animal return—and then before they could do more than prepare to move from the water the baboons would shout again.

Through long days that game of waitings and warnings would continue. When their own youngsters were close at hand and the sandbank was deserted, the baboons, though nervous and watchful, would be for the most part quiet even though the crocodiles were at hand; but if a crocodile stirred, or the shadow to a wind-blown leaf gave the appearance of water moving in the channel, uproar would begin once more.

Only when the channel was empty of crocodiles and no still, grey bodies could be seen in the river, were the baboons at peace; and only then would the smaller animals come to drink.

CHAPTER
TWENTY

CROCODILE AND RHINOCEROS: A DUEL
OF GIANTS

THE elephants still bathed and drank in the
river, quite unconcerned about the presence
of crocodiles and disregarding the warnings of the
baboons. A herd of buffalo came to drink, and
at the sight of them the giant crocodile would
linger in the middle of the pool, afraid to approach the herd but hoping vainly that a single
animal would linger behind. The old rhinoceros
who shared the summit of a hill with the leopard
would come by his own well-worn path to drink
at the end of his day's feed, and him also the
crocodile would watch from a distance, realising
more and more as the days passed and the smaller
animals became more difficult to catch, what a
magnificent meal the great creature would provide.
And the lion, when in the evening he had killed
despite the shy watchfulness of the herds, would

come to drink, with caution but nevertheless with a knowledge of his own mightiness; and him too the crocodile would watch from afar, not venturing to approach.

But all the lesser animals, the zebra, the impalla and other gazelle, the waterbuck, the wildebeest and the kongoni, were benefited by the caution of the baboons who had come to the rock close beside the river; and though they now drank less at the times of their own choosing, they drank with far greater safety and with less toll upon their numbers.

The smaller crocodiles and the mate of the giant ate the larger fish in the river and might occasionally snatch a baby hippo whose mother was careless, and thus were not severely troubled by the absence of the greater feasts which in the past had followed a successful hunt at the sandbank. But the giant's appetite required meat, and when several days passed without a kill he became ravenous and desperate. Then he was more venturesome, ignoring the warnings of baboons and sometimes walking openly on to the sandbank and even to the beginning of the undergrowth to stand and look for a possible prey. But though he was clear-sighted over the water, his eyes were

unaccustomed to the confusing shadows of close
country, and he soon grew tired of watching
bushes without any certainty that animals were
amongst them. Then he would go back to the
water, swim round and round the pool, thinking
of great feasts of the past, of the strange new
animals by the bridge for whom he had once
longed and whom he had hunted so disastrously.

More than once he considered whether he
should seek some other part of the river where
hunting might be easier, or even go back to his
former quarters, close to the bridge. But at that
thought the old pain beneath his front leg would
seem to return, with a strange stiffness of the
muscles which he had never quite lost, and he
would be reminded that even the pangs of hunger
and the difficulty of catching shy animals were
better than the pain that came from hunting
creatures who retaliated and killed.

So the giant stayed in the pool, daily becoming
more daring and more vicious with the in-
sufficiency of his meals. He drew near to the
buffalo, on the edge of the herd, considering
whether he could dart in and seize the outermost
animal and drag it below the water before the
others could turn and gore him with their horns;

but always he hesitated too long, so that with a toss of their heads the animals finished drinking and departed before he had made his attack. He came closer, too, to the lions, during the first light of daybreak, sometimes coming so near that the lion would see the uneven snout against the silver of the water as he lowered his head to drink, and would step back alarmed. And, greater plans having failed, the crocodile would float silently upon the surface, thinking once more of the gigantic form of the rhinoceros, which would provide food for many a day.

On one side of the leopard's hill, furthest from that animal's den and the crag from which it watched the plain, the pebbly surface of the ground was worn into a path. By the beginning of this path, close-growing bushes and thorns formed a fortress, ring-shaped, in which lived the old rhinoceros. Though he knew of no enemies except the lion and possible natives, he was suspicious and anxious for protection; and by keeping always to one entrance to his home, a tunnel through entangled undergrowth, he had allowed its walls, in the course of many years, to grow so thick that no animal could penetrate them.

He was a creature of habit, keeping regularly to set times for his daily occupations and to set paths for his journeys. He left the hill always in the afternoon, as the heat waned, walking by the path to the edge of the steep slope and then sliding on his hind-quarters to the bottom. There he started to feed, grazing off grass, roots and the leaves of thorn trees that grew round the foot of the hill, always keeping within a few feet of the same track, along the north side of the hill, till he reached the opposite side from that which he had descended, and then turning away by the well-worn path which he had followed daily for year after year, still feeding but at the same time making his way slowly towards the river where he would drink at the end of his meal.

One day, when the leopard cubs on the further side of the hill had grown sufficiently to be able to go with their parents to hunt, the rhinoceros set out as usual, making his way to the river by slow stages. In the thick undergrowth not far from the edge of the pool, thorns scraped against his hide and low branches of trees swung against his head and his horn. But such obstacles made no impression on him, and he continued down the path which he had so often trodden,

164

THE BABOON.

" The rhinoceros lowered his head to browse."

leaving it only once when he pushed his way through some low scrub and lowered his head to browse.

He came to the edge of the sandbank. Only a little while before, the elephants had departed and herds of zebra and kongoni had taken their place, drinking plentifully until a warning shout from the baboons had made them bolt to safety. Now, only a few minutes after that scare, the sandbank was deserted. The baboons sat on the summit of their rock, the two youngsters close beside their mother, for they knew that the giant crocodile still lingered a few yards from the shore.

As the rhinoceros approached the water the baboons shouted again. The old animal stopped, his ears went forward to listen, and then, drawing confidence from the fact that the parasite birds remained undisturbed on his back, he again advanced. He wanted to drink as he drank daily, always at the same hour, always at the same spot on the sandbank, and he was not deterred by the sounds of excitement that came from the rock as the baboons saw the crocodile come steadily but silently closer.

The rhinoceros lowered his head so that his

mouth touched the water. And instantly the now ravenous crocodile seized him.

Feeling those terrible teeth pierce his skin and then clench immovably together, holding him in a vice-like grip, the rhinoceros tried to draw back, but found that he could not; and at the same instant he felt himself pulled forward towards the pool. With his feet pressing the sand and his body drawn back so that his hind-quarters were against the ground, he in his turn pulled, getting his mouth just clear of the water. The crocodile held on, pressing backwards, his feet against the sloping sandbank, his tail threshing the water, his teeth still clenched, all of his huge strength concentrated on the struggle. The rhinoceros's legs slipped forward, pressing up little ridges of wet sand in front of them, and bringing him an inch nearer to death. Then with renewed effort, he tried to wrench his jaw sideways out of the encompassing grip, but the weight of the crocodile held him, and in the fruitless moment of that change of plan he slipped still further forward. With every muscle taut, he pulled backward, his hind feet now digging further into the sand; the sudden effort regained for him an inch of ground, then that was won

back from him, his feet slipped again, his front
legs entered the water.

He was snorting and frantic with terror. He
hardly felt the pain of his mangled and bleeding
jaw, but he saw the stretch of water before him
and the giant body of his enemy, the lashing tail
that beat the water, the two small eyes fixed
relentlessly on his own. He felt himself slip, he
knew that already his mouth was only a few inches
above the water. With even greater effort, born
of his terror, he pulled, raising his rump so that
his hind legs could find fresh purchase in the
sand, further from the edge of the water; and
he pulled with feelings of despair as that fresh
purchase failed him, his feet slipped back to their
old position, the two ridges of sand moved
forward, his head seemed to be drawn away from
his shoulders, his front legs moved further
into the water—he felt himself drawn with infinite
but irresistible slowness into the pool.

For a minute he still struggled after his mouth
was below the surface, once jerking up his head
in frantic suffocation and receiving respite from
one quick gulp of air before he was pulled
onward and downward and the water of the pool
finally closed upon his body.

CHAPTER
TWENTY-ONE

IMPALLA'S JOY

WHEN the young impalla first joined the other gazelle near the river-bank, she felt a new sense of calmness because she was at last amongst creatures of her own race. With baboons, elephants and zebra, she had had nothing in common. Actively, as the baboons had done, or passively like the elephants, they might protect her from danger, but she had no instincts in common with them and they could never give her any sense of companionship.

That, it was true, she had had amongst the zebra, because of her friendship with the one inexperienced young male. Yet even there, though she had been warmed and comforted by him and though his mother had grown to feel a protective interest in her, she had always been a stranger to the rest of the herd. Her presence had been tolerated and she had come at times to feel at home; yet though she had shared the life of the herd, they had never adopted her as one of themselves.

With the gazelle it was different. Though of another species, she also was a gazelle. She had not the same markings as the animals of this herd, she had characteristics of her own, she frequently leapt in the air, either in expression of her joy or in terror, while they, like the zebra, jumped only when startled by a snake or some other creature on the ground. Yet she was made welcome. When the first old male zebra had come to inspect her he had butted her with his nose as if to ask contemptuously who or what she was; but the old male gazelle who first approached her came in friendly manner, eager for her history and quite obviously pleased at her arrival.

For a week she lived in contentment. The gazelle were shy and very cautious, their sentinels being always ready to set the herd bolting at the slightest suspicion. The drawing back of the water in the pool as the dry season advanced made them use even greater care when they came to drink, and although a kongoni was once snatched by the crocodile while they were on the

sandbank, sending them with many other animals
scampering at once to safety, the gazelle themselves suffered no loss. Drinking, grazing,
resting or sleeping, they were confident of the
vigilance of trusted sentinels; and as the days
passed the impalla, sharing that confidence, forgot
her fears.

But as boldness returned to her, so also did her
restlessness. Happiness with the gazelle did not
keep her thoughts from the still greater happiness
which she would know among her own herd.
Often, as she grazed, she would move to one side
and stand gazing into the distance; or signs in the
grass that other animals had passed would attract
her and she would wander by herself to inspect
them; not wandering far afield as she had done
on the day when the wild dogs had pursued her,
but nevertheless leaving the compactness of the
herd and standing at a little distance on a stretch
of open grass.

One day, while thus by herself, the signs on
the ground told that a herd of zebra had recently
crossed the small plain on which she stood. She
became interested, following the irregular trail,
parallel with the route of the gazelle and gradually becoming more and more sure that these

zebra were known to her and that if she could overtake them she would find amongst them the young male who had been her friend.

She came to a glade, where patches of sunlight piercing the trees were interlaced with broad lines of shade. Zebra were grazing there and, her sudden delight making her leap in the air, the impalla saw that her friend was amongst them. She ran towards him, greeting him nose to nose, then sniffing at his flanks, circling round him, leaping for joy once more, and then staying in deep contentment to graze beside him.

Though less excited than she, the zebra gave her sniff for sniff, watching her as she leapt and feeling a stolid pleasure in her return. Their noses touched as they grazed, and he in his turn was content.

The gazelle grazed onward in the direction of the river, crossing the glade and leaving it for another stretch of open country. As they realised that the impalla was no longer with them, some of them turned to stare doubtfully back towards the trees. But she did not raise her head. She was not thinking of the future, of what would happen if she deserted the gazelle, of whether by rejoining the zebra she would gain or lose in happiness; the present gave her joy and she had no other thought. The grass of that glade seemed sweeter than any that she had recently tasted.

Suddenly, however, and only a few minutes later, she did lift her head, answering a deep instinct which drew her eyes to look across the glade. There, walking across the alternate bars of sun and shade, went a herd of impalla. The backs of some were golden brown, caught by the unfiltered sun; others were dark in the shadows of the trees.

She forgot, in that moment, the young zebra beside her, the gazelle now making their way to the river, the terrors and dangers that had oppressed her. She leapt in the air, then ran, then leapt again, crossing the intervening space, coming amongst the impalla, her own herd of impalla, the friends she had lost and now regained. She ran beside a buck who stood in the sunlight, leapt around him, pressed her nose against the neck of a doe, leapt and ran in transports of delight. The doe, knowing her lost offspring, began to lick the young impalla's face, her throat, her flanks. She stood trembling, knowing a joy that had no equal.

" There, walking across the alternate bars of sun and shade,
went a herd of impalla."

ZEBRA   IMPALLA   THOMPSON'S GAZELLES

" The gazelles grazed onward in the direction of the river,"

" The impalla, her own herd of impalla, the friends she had lost
and now regained."

CHAPTER TWENTY-TWO

CROCODILES AT WAR

DURING the days that followed his victory over the rhinoceros the giant crocodile became increasingly arrogant.

Without his being fully conscious of it, the spear-head which had wounded him in his first encounter with men had left more than a scar and stiffened muscles; it had been a wound also to his self-confidence. Till then he had been aware of his great size and strength, of the terror that he inspired, and of the fact that though animals on the bank might escape him through their shyness, they hardly ever got away when once his silent waiting had ended and his attack had begun.

Still possessed by that confidence, he had attacked the woman who lingered at the water's edge beside the bridge—and not only had his prey escaped almost from his jaws, but he had received a reminder of his defeat which still occasionally pained him, even though months had passed. The sub-conscious effect of that wound was immediate; when with the two other crocodiles he had lain in wait for the men a few days later, he had chosen a position at some distance, he had not ventured in pursuit of the "ostrich," and when the men had come with more of their iron-headed spears he had not only fled, but had at once decided to move to a fresh stretch of the river.

In the peacefulness and easy hunting of the pool some of his old confidence had returned, and he had accepted it as natural that the two smaller crocodiles should be afraid of him and should keep out of his path; but even then his self-esteem was less sure than it had once been, so that when the arrival of the baboons by the water-side made his hunting more difficult he became hesitant, until sheer hunger forced him to be daring.

But now, after that gigantic struggle so victoriously ended, the whole of his confidence was restored. Who else in the river could have won that victory? What other creature would have dared to seize almost the biggest of the land-animals or, daring, would have been able to drag it beneath the water?

It was good, too, to feed off that gigantic carcase, with his mate beside him, knowing that there was now a sufficiency of food for many days. It protruded from the hollow in the bank, one end rising to the surface of the water so that ripples, as the crocodile passed, broke on it like little waves. When he swam out of his creek he saw that grey-black lump of flesh and knew with pride and self-satisfaction that it was his own, to be shared with none but his mate.

Yet one morning he saw the two other crocodiles of the pool not many yards away, their small eyes fixed longingly on the prize. Though their appetites were more easily satisfied with fish, they nevertheless were accustomed to take animals occasionally from the sandbank, and the vigilance of the baboons had made hunting difficult for them, just as it had done for the giant, so that the knowledge that a great carcase, ready for eating, lay easily within reach had tempted them to come nearer to the creek than they would otherwise have dared to do.

To the giant crocodile, in his mood of assertiveness, that impertinence was like a challenge.

He swam to drive the intruders away and chased them until they took shelter in the fastness of their own creek.

He was pleased at the quickness with which they turned tail at his approach; it was yet another tribute to his power. And he enjoyed the pursuit, knowing that he could easily catch them if he wished.

Thereafter he chased them across the pool whenever he saw them. He no longer allowed them to share the island for basking in the heat of the day but, swimming at half his greatest speed, he drove them to their own home. Sometimes, to add to the pleasure of the chase, he would cut them off from their creek, chivying them twice round the pool before he allowed them to escape. And once, when by good fortune or skill they had eluded the watchfulness of the baboons and captured a young kongoni at the sandbank, he chased them until they were compelled to abandon their prize, so that he could drag it home to his already over-filled larder.

Under this treatment the life of the two smaller crocodiles soon became intolerable. All the ease of their existence was dispelled. It was impossible for them to stay in their creek, for their larders

were soon emptied and they were forced to come
to the pool for fish, or to the sandbank for meat.
Their creek lay in a curve of the bank, against
which the water was shallow; consequently even
for fish they had to swim out towards the centre
of the pool. Then one of them would sight a
large fish and swim towards it, but before he
could snap there would be a swirl in the water
and the giant crocodile would appear from
the further side of the island, as if he alone
might eat or swim in that stretch of the river.
Or else the two would come cautiously across
the pool, slipping silently towards the sandbank, hoping to be able to ensconce themselves in the channel before being discovered.
Sometimes they failed and were driven back;
sometimes they succeeded, but were thwarted in
their hunting by the shouts of the baboons;
occasionally they hunted successfully, but were
prevented by the giant from dragging their victim
back to the creek. They would try a longer but
more shadowed route round the edge of the
pool, keeping mostly beneath overhanging trees,
but there was one stretch of uncovered bank
where they were forced to show themselves, and
then the giant would come, swimming straight

towards them with his blunt jaw just above the surface. Then they had no choice but to go onwards, knowing that with his far greater strength he would overtake them, even if they were not handicapped by the weight of a dragging carcase. Once, turning aside, they swam into a small creek not far from their own and there waited till the giant moved away, when, still clinging to their victim, they went home, for once triumphant. And once, when they were particularly hungry and reckless, they held on to their meat even when the giant snapped at it, so that they left him with the greater portion while they retained the less eatable head and shoulders.

Those two partial triumphs restored their courage, making them believe that by greater daring and resource they might yet escape their enemy. Thereafter they became cunning. When they had hunted successfully one would drag the meat round the darkened edge of the pool, while the other, showing itself, would entice the giant in the opposite direction.

For a while these tactics were successful, the giant being led to chase the female crocodile across the pool while the male unobtrusively made his way homeward with the prize. But presently the giant became suspicious. He was puzzled at the ease with which he now sighted one of the crocodiles, at the fact that to all appearances only one now went back from the sandbank. And with suspicion, grew vindictiveness. Hitherto he had been content to chase and to chivy, drawing satisfaction from the speed with which the other crocodiles swam from him, from a sense of his own power and superiority. But when he suspected that his bullying was without avail, that these puny and insignificant crocodiles were smuggling their captures past him, anger possessed him. He was no longer content to chivy, and his chasing acquired a purpose.

. . . . .

The female crocodile, making her way across the pool, became suddenly aware of something different about the giant who pursued her. Generally he would swim quietly, following her however much she turned or changed her course, his head always within a few feet of her tail. But now he took advantage of his greater speed, drawing alongside and ahead of her, circling round her, watching her with eyes that she knew to be threatening. Whereas recently her terror of him had grown less as she realised that he had no

object but to irritate, that terror now suddenly
returned with full force. He was more than twice
as big as she was, far bigger also than her mate;
though she recognised that he was a crocodile like
herself, she regarded him with loathing, as a
monster and evil. So, seeing the threats in his
small, greedy eyes while he swam round and
round her, she suddenly turned and swam back
towards her mate, terror adding to her speed.

The giant turned too, swimming at her side,
crossing in front of her, dropping behind, swiftly
overtaking her, lashing the water with his tail
as his anger increased.

The male crocodile, laboriously dragging the
body of a young zebra under the overhanging
branches of trees, saw the foam cast up by the
lashing of that tail and knew that his mate was
in danger. Letting go of the carcase he swam
towards the middle of the pool. Seeing him
coming, the giant suddenly ceased to circle. He
was at that moment a few feet behind the tail of
the female crocodile; he swam forward, drew
close beside her, and snapped viciously, his teeth
entering her hide over and under her left front
leg, piercing flesh and crunching bone, to meet
and interlock. Then with a wrench he drew

180

away, blood trickling between his teeth, a larger stain of red spreading on the surface of the water beside the wounded crocodile.

The male crocodile saw that sudden snap; as he drew nearer he saw small drops of blood still falling from the giant's teeth. His tail lashed the water in fury and he swam to attack.

In strength as in speed he was no match for the giant. If he had fled, trying to get back to the security of his home, he would very quickly have been overtaken, and the gigantic teeth would have closed upon him before he could turn and defend himself. But when he attacked, he had one point of superiority—because he was smaller he could turn more swiftly to bring his teeth against some vulnerable point in the giant's hide.

The giant, facing him, swam forward with jaws open. But the smaller crocodile did not stay to meet the attack. He turned, swam away to the left, turned again and then swam swiftly forward so that his teeth would meet the giant's less protected body, away from the menace of the jaw. The giant turned too, less quickly yet away from danger; and his enemy, failing to bite as he had intended, could do no more than swing his tail, bringing it with a crashing blow against the side of the giant's head, a little below and behind his ear.

If the positions had been reversed, if the smaller crocodile had been struck with the full force of the giant's tail, he would have been stunned; and death from those sharp, triangular teeth would have come before he could recover consciousness. But the weight of the smaller tail could not stun the giant, nor do anything more than cause him to stagger slightly in the water and to become more furious, more intent on putting a speedy end to his enemy. His tail lashed from side to side and beat the water, turning the smooth surface into waves and sending clouds of spray flying one across the other. The smaller crocodile moved similarly in a flying mist of foam caused by the frantic lashings of his own tail—the water around them was like a whirlpool. Again the giant crocodile turned, swimming away in a wide circle to do so, again he came forward, with enormous speed but with little nicety of manœuvring. The fight was between Goliath and David, between huge strength, ill controlled, and quickness backed by cunning. The smaller crocodile came forward to meet the giant's attack, so that

182

for a minute they advanced jaw against jaw. Then, before the giant could realise what was happening, his enemy swung sharply away to the left, and turned very rapidly, stemming his advance as he did so. The giant, still borne by the momentum of his great speed, shot past, only then, when it was too late, beginning to turn. And at that moment the smaller crocodile, safe himself from teeth and tail, swam quickly forward and bit into the giant's neck, his teeth piercing the hide, checking for an instant against bone, and then crushing down close to where head was joined to spine.

For a few seconds he remained there, his jaws still slowly closing through mangled flesh and splintered bone, whilst the giant in his agony thrashed the water. Then, sure of his victory, the smaller crocodile drew away.

The giant, mortally injured, did not renew the attack. For several minutes his tail continued to churn the water, then the movements grew unsteady. Weakly he swam towards the shore by the sandbank, the swing of his tail becoming every minute more feeble. Within a yard of the sandbank he was almost inert; the tail moved once, almost idly, like the final swing of a slow pendulum. His body turned on its side and rolled over; and he lay dead, his gigantic form just clear of the water.

.   .   .   .   .

The baboons, seated on their rock, shouted as the body neared the shore, then gesticulated with excitement as they saw its lifelessness. For some time they were noisy, shouting and chattering, until the stillness of the dead form wearied them. Motionless, with the yellow skin of its belly now uppermost, it remained until a solitary jackal came to drink. Seeing it, he darted back into the safety of the bushes, his thirst unquenched. Then a vulture sighted it and planed down, his sudden earthward plunge acting as a signal to others who flew nearer, hovered for a moment, swooped and landed. For a minute they stood watching; then, with the coming of certainty that the crocodile was dead, they moved forward. Kites and marabou storks joined them, the jackal returned with others of his kind, no longer afraid since the sight of the vultures had told him of death, but with joy at so great a scavenging. A feathered hedge appeared about the carcase, moving and swaying as jackals tried to approach, as vultures struggled to pierce the hide and quarrelled over

"For several minutes his tail continued to churn the water."

" A feathered hedge appeared about the carcase."

small titbits, as self-assertive birds climbed across the body in their eagerness.

While the heat of the sun grew, blazed into inescapable intensity and faded slowly to the cool of the evening, the scavenging continued. The herd of impalla, coming through the bushes to drink, stopped at the edge of the sandbank, half anticipating a warning shout from the baboons; then as no shout came, they advanced, to stop a moment later at the sight of vultures feeding so close to the water. The birds, disturbed by the sudden approach of the animals, rose for a moment into the air, and the youngest of the herd felt once more a sharp spasm of terror at the sight of the giant crocodile; then, seeing the older impalla standing motionless, suspicious but unafraid as the vultures settled once more to their feast, she came gingerly forward to stand close beside the leader of the herd. By the same instinct which had told the baboons of the presence of death, backed by the sight of the scavengers, she realised then why the gigantic form of the crocodile lay so motionless.

The leader of the impalla, turning from his direct path towards the water, went to a corner of the sandbank, the rest of the herd following him. He looked once towards the dead crocodile, then lowered his head to drink. Other herds, the zebra, kongoni and gazelle, a pair of ostriches, wart-hogs, guinea-fowl and eland, moved likewise to the sides of the sandbank, leaving the centre, with its grim feast, avoided. Now and then a bird, fed to repletion, would turn to drink from the river and then run across the sandbank with wings desperately flapping as it tried to raise its over-weighted body from the ground. One by one the vultures left, rising at last and flying to their roosting places among boulders or in the trees; more slowly the marabou storks and kites followed.

That day's scavenging was finished. In the night hyenas and jackals would gather to the feast; with the coming of daylight the vultures would settle once more upon the now diminished carcase, while others came from a distance as the news spread through the forest. And by the second morning there would be little left but bones lying at the edge of the sandbank to mark the end of the giant crocodile whose ravages had for so long spread terror through the valley.

CHAPTER
TWENTY-THREE

RAIN

THE sun set in an angry sky, heavy with blue-grey clouds. As the last edging of red faded to white, in turn to be overlapped with grey, silence settled upon the valley, broken only by the low moaning of a rising wind among the tree-tops.

The animals moved quietly, disturbed by the oppressive heat and aware of the threat that underlay the silence. The impalla, close beside the friendly herd of zebra, moved forward warily, afraid, yet uncertain of the direction from which danger would come. They kept close together, seeking comfort in proximity, raising their heads to sniff the wind, jostling one another, turning every now and then to stare with undefined alarm into the darkness.

Then, to usher in the first moments of a new season, thunder rolled, and again and again the darkness that had spread across the valley was broken by the flash of lightning. Suddenly the rain came. Big drops fell, then with an increasing downpour the drops ceased to be separate and water fell from the split heavens like a great cascade. In the place of that unearthly silence the crash of great reports stood out amid a dim sound of distant drumming. Flash succeeded flash, light stepping anew into the path of light so that darkness ended and trees were seen suddenly gaunt and black in the lightness of unnatural night.

On the parched earth, streams formed, the dry dongas began to fill and the shallow dips in undulating country became moist with the beginnings of pools. The animals shivered and trembled, heads bowed, the rain beating on their bodies. They stood in compact groups, no longer guarded by sentinels for this was no danger from which they could escape. The lion had taken shelter in his lair, the leopard and the cheetah lay under overhanging rocks where new streams broke beside them into tiny waterfalls, the packs of wild dogs were grouped together under trees. The storm ruled the valley, putting all creatures in subjection.

But before two hours had passed, the rain ceased. From afar off the noise of thunder still came in muffled reverberation from the mountains, but the darkness was now unbroken by lightning and in place of silence that threatened and the crashing noises of the storm there came a stillness of new peace. Into it came the hoot of an owl moving in its shelter among the leaves, the sudden laugh of a jackal, and the call of a rock-rabbit as it came to peer from its rocky home into the awakened valley. The impalla shook themselves, rubbed against each other's flanks, raised their heads into the new coolness of the air and moved forward. They stopped beside newly formed pools, drank, and passed on. And as they went, the youngest of them suddenly started to leap in the air, first forwards, then sideways, again and again. She was no longer afraid nor desolate. In this world which with the coming of the rain seemed newly created, she was at last among her friends, contented and entirely happy.

THE END

PRINTED BY J. AND J. GRAY, EDINBURGH